# THE BUFFALO WALLOW

# THE BUFFALO
# WALLOW

## *A Prairie Boyhood*

by

## CHARLES TENNEY JACKSON
### "Jack Tennison"

UNIVERSITY OF NEBRASKA PRESS · LINCOLN

*First Bison Book printing September, 1967*

**Bison Book edition reproduced from the first edition by arrangement with the Bobbs-Merrill Company, Inc.**

# CONTENTS

# THE BUFFALO WALLOW

# 1

# Where Four Roads Met

---

**W**E LIVED in the middle of everything. No doubt of that. Cousin Ellis and I could go out to the section corner where the ranch stood, dig down in the prairie sod and feel a rusty iron stake that the surveyors had placed when folks first settled this country ten years ago. Mighty snowdrifts almost buried the sod house behind us, but where the roads crossed the blizzard winds had swept a space bare.

The iron was so cold that your fingers stuck to it. Ellis stood up and blew on them. "Here she is, Chick. We're right in the middle of America. You can see it on the Joggerfee map."

I tried to open the old Geography in the wind. "We sure are. One road goes Down South. One Out West. One Back East. One Up North. Soon's spring comes we'll start explorin' 'em. Don't tell anybody. Aunt Effie'd just laugh. Lige'd tell us to go ahead, travel till we got too hungry."

"Tackle South Road first. Won't be so cold. Besides, you see it on the map. South Road goes on and on until you run right into the ocean."

"Yeh, but first you run into Rebels an' start 'em all up yellin' again. Lige says when he was in the Tennessee Army them Johnny Rebs could scare a man yellin'."

The war had been over more than fifteen years, but there might be some Rebels left, and you'd have to sneak past them to find the ocean at the end of South Road. Ellis was kicking his copper-toed boots against frozen ruts. I looked back at the soddy behind the drifts, the windmill glittering in white, the rusty barbed-wire corral, the corncrib, the big piles of wheat and corn piled on the ground with the pot-bellied home-herd cows pawing into them, the straw barn, with a few chickens, turkeys, ducks venturing out as the sun rose. Beyond that a snow-buried line of little cottonwoods, the windbreak which didn't break any wind; and beyond that the plowed North Eighty, and beyond that again the unbroken prairie glittering to the rim of the world.

We turned back from the middle of America with chattering teeth. Yes, sir, no doubt of it: South Road was marked right on the map! Years later, vast with learning, I found that this line on the map was 98 degrees, west longitude, and quite a way from Lige's corner, but when I was eight you'd have had a time proving it to me. Here we were, right on that line, where the four roads crossed and led into lands of mystery!

I ran for the house with the Joggerfee book. I had also a Second Reader which I couldn't get out of because I didn't have any other. I had a slate too, and a tattered arithmetic which I couldn't make sense of and wouldn't try. A lot of stuff in school would just pester you, so don't try to understand. Let Teacher holler.

In the soddy, in Effie's leather trunk under the bed, were three other books, but we rarely saw them. The trunk had come out in Lige's covered wagon when folks first came into this prairie country. One book was the Bible, wrapped in old newspaper and tied with string, which Effie said her mother had given her Back East, and she wasn't going to take it out where anybody could get their dirty paws on it. One old tattered book was all about medicine, and sometimes Lige wanted to see it about how to physic a horse when it got colic, but he didn't dare meddle in Effie's trunk. And the third book was just plumb mystery and we couldn't get our dirty paws on it either. It was a faded pink book with little flowers on the cover, and Lige said that in it was the dangest nonsense you ever heard of. But Effie would get this book out sometimes and read by the oil lamp, and her eyes would shine and she'd smile and look far off into mystery.

This book was kept under a lot of musty clothes which had come from Back East, and Effie never had a place to wear them out in our prairie country, when she got to town only perhaps once a year, with Lige when he had to haul grain enough to pay Intrust on the Mortgage.

Lige said, "That-there book, it's a storybook. I never read it, but, afore we was married, Effie used to read it to me. Two fellers was after the same girl, an', doggone, one feller tells this girl he can't live without her."

"Why can't he?" I asked. "Don't make sense."

"Sure, but no use askin' Effie now. Don't you an' Ellis ever get hands on that book or Effie'll give you conniption fits."

"I don't want the dang book. I don't want any book."

Ellis said, "Yeh, we do. The ol' Joggerfee book what shows where South Road goes an' Chick an' me aim to foller it someday." He looked anxiously at his pa. "Could we have ol' Tops an' Jewel to ride when you ain't workin' 'em someday?"

I said, "That-there South Road winds up right in the ocean on the map. The ocean's marked blue, an' a little pink whale's in it."

"Whales?" roared Lige, his thin whiskers wagging. "Sure! You boys never saw a fish yet, but this ocean's full of 'em! An' the ocean's so wide you can't see across it, an' it's so salt you can't drink it. Only water you boys ever saw is rain an' what comes outa the windmill pipe. You don't know much."

Well, maybe so. But I didn't believe all Lige said, like that the world was round like a turnip, when I could look on the level prairie and see it wasn't. Lige could tell some whoppers when we were snowed in nights, him an' Earl Staley, our last cowhand, playing seven-up, Effie gone to bed and Ellis and I hanging around to warm up before we went out in the lean-to to turn in. It was a frosty place to sleep in, and you had to run quick, slide under the covers and stop shivering. Only warm place was right by the cookstove in the soddy, and everybody sat close as they could get. Effie would be in bed right above her trunk where her storybook was. Nobody knew yet how that book would get Earl in a fix where he had to quit cow-punching, and would get a sheriff chasing after me.

# 2

# First Breakin' of the Last Prairie

ON WINTER mornings Ellis always beat me to the warmest spot, behind the cookstove, back to the wall, where he twisted hay from the wood box which had never held any wood since it too came out from Wisconsin in the covered wagon. There was no firewood in this country, not a stick. A boy could hardly find anything to make an arrow if he wanted to play bow 'n' arrow. Central Nebraska. The early eighties.

Ellis shoved his hay twists into the open firebox, and I put big ears of yellow corn on the quick brief blaze. We had dug the last of the frozen cobs from under the drifts outside the door which slanted clear over the soddy. Lige's coal was always gone by March, but snow wasn't. Well, Ellis and I got the fire to snapping good. I had to reach past Lige's legs to get the corn in. Lige was in front of the stove warming his hands over plates. Earl, our cowhand, was on the side with his feet in the oven. Aunt Effie was trying to start breakfast, a pan of sody biscuits in her hands as she edged near the stove.

She said, "You menfolks git back from that stove. Git your hoofs outa that oven. Lands, a body can't bake a batch o' cookies without 'em tastin' like ol' wool socks an'

13

wet boots! Chick, you hustle that fire. Earl, you shove back now. Hustle!"

Our cowhand took his feet out of the oven. He shoved back the snowy bridles from the stove top where they were thawing so that frozen bits wouldn't peel the lips of his cow pony. Earl was sure discouraged, and what Lige said next made him feel worse. Lige was gazing dreamily out the one small window which Ellis and I had opened through the drift outside.

"Well, sir, she's meltin'. Icicles drippin'. Spring's about here, an' now I aim to break that West Eighty. Yes-sir-bobbee, last dang wild prairie on this ranch."

Earl felt so bad that he went outdoors and gazed south toward Texas. Ellis and I felt no better. By spring a boy's copper-toed boots were full of holes and he twisted his feet around in ice water, but what Lige had said made me twist them with panic. Ellis hollered at his pa, "Aw, what you want to break the West Eighty fer? It'll be just weeds higher 'n your head like all the other land you plowed. Last prairie we got."

Lige gazed on dreamily out to the vast glitter of melting snow. "Corn. First-breakin' corn. You boys big enough to help now. Ellis can jab holes in the furrows with a stick, an' Chick can drap seed. Corn. Big first-breakin' corn. If Earl'd stay——"

"He won't stay! Ever hear of a cow rider stickin' around when he hears o' farmwork? Mebbe last cowhand in this county."

Effie slammed shut the oven door. "I hope so. That Earl, he's just like all the other hands I fed all winters. Board 'em for chores, an' come spring——"

"Chores!" I yelled. "Cowhands don't do chores. Ellis an' me do all the chores. Earl says it makes his hands sore to milk."

"Now you made him feel bad talkin' about farmwork," said Ellis.

"He don't feel so bad he can't come in an' eat." Effie rattled plates on the oilclothed table between the stove and the sheet partition across the end of the sod house where she and Lige slept. Lige was never able to get up and dress without tearing this sheet wall half down while Effie stated her opinion of cowhands and farmers, which was awful to hear. The one chore Earl did was to get the fire started for Effie, who'd appear after further convulsions of the wall.

"Saw some steaks, Earl. Land, ain't the fire goin' yet? Well, what can't be cured must be endured. Lige, stir the mush."

Earl would vanish into the clapboard lean-to where Ellis and I slept. Our outer bedcover was an old buffalo skin, the hair mostly worn off. Fine hard snow would sift through the clapboards onto this and onto the floor of frozen dirt. At the foot of our bed hung the frozen carcass from which Earl sawed meat. He started at the rump and by spring was sawing close to the critter's ears. We called it all steak. Earl went back with an armful of steaks, and I watched the carcass gyrate on the rope.

The first thing a dear little child saw in the glad morning was the red insides of a dead cow. Ellis and I would grab our frozen boots and run into the soddy. First there got the warmest place. Menfolks always got their feet into the oven first, but Effie chased them away first too. Behind the stove was safer, but we had to keep the fire going, piling the big corn ears on the snapping hay, until everybody warmed up some. Ellis and I never had shoes. From last freeze to first freeze we ran barefooted. Knee-high stiff leather boots were a winter-long torture, but we had to have them. Effie proclaimed, "What can't be cured must be endured. Git your boots off the stove or you don't eat. Lands!"

Ellis and I thawed and twisted our boots on with howls and grunts and shouts of the four Indian words we had learned at school. Some boy said they were Pawnee and terrible cusswords. But nobody at home knew them, so you could yell them at Teacher, Earl or any fool cow safely. When our feet were down at last in the soggy wool socks Ellis and I limped out to get away from the wind by the cow barn. That is, what was left of the cow barn.

Spring was about here! We knew it by the holes in our boots and by seeing that the milk cows had eaten up their barn. The crazy cottonwood-pole frame stuck through the snow like skinned bones. Range cattle didn't get any barn, which was why their bodies began to show all over the last unbroken land. Sign of spring, dead cows! And the barn eaten up. We had built that barn last fall when the threshing machine had spewed straw all over the top and sides of the pole frame many feet thick. A grand place to play, dark and warm holiday week, but all winter the milk cows inside had chewed and wallowed and pushed until there was as much snow inside as out. And all winter Ellis and I had to battle them from the big snow-covered heaps of corn and wheat that Lige had piled back of the corral with a few rusty strands of barbed wire around them for a fence. This was an unending battle. The range stock raided in. We could ride them off, but the tame milk cows didn't care a hoot for two half-frozen boys afoot or horseback. Neither did Effie. She stuck her head out of the soddy door after menfolks had been chased from the house. "Lige, you go help run them critters off that corn pile afore they founder."

"Where's Earl? He can help. I don't aim to fool with cows now."

"That cowhand, he sneaks somewhere soon as he eats. How much range stuff he supposed to run anyway? How much you got left?"

"Dang if I know. Don't want no cow business any more. Corn——"

"Corn—corn—corn! Crib full an' busted, and then you pile it higher 'n the house an' let it rot. Ain't worth haulin' to town, even if a team could get there. Seven cents a bushel—an' what you plant next?"

"Corn. Break the West Eighty soon as ground thaws. Corn——"

Ellis and I could hear from the corral gate.

Ellis said, "There Lige goes again—breakin' the last prairie we got. Why don't Effie bust him with that skillet? Chick, what we do if Lige starts his dang rollin'-cutter into West Eighty?"

"Mebbe we could bust his cutter afore he starts. Mebbe we could get a lariat on it, bust it off the plow an' snake it somewheres a long way. He can't plow prairie without the rollin'-cutter."

I was little and skinny, just about high enough to drink

out of a crock of buttermilk, Effie said. Now I looked out across the South Eighty where a few broken cornstalks showed above the drifts. I looked past the corral to the East Eighty, but that timothy pasture showed nothing but a few fence posts. I looked at the North Eighty, but the old wheat stubble was all buried. We could still hear Effie jawin' Lige at the soddy.

"Go round up yore pore dumb critters. I bet you got dead cows from here to Platte Bottoms froze stiff 'n' dead."

"Suits me. No more cow business. Corn. Buckwheat too. Mebbe millet an' sorghum an'——"

"Corn? What we feed an' bed a cowhand all winter fer?"

"Dang if I know. Them fellers just come to this ranch an' stay all winter. They know we're bustin' with feed fer their ponies, an' I like to play seven-up snowed in evenin's. Then——"

"Sure, then come spring them cowhands light out fer Texas."

"Suits me. I don't wanta hear cow critters mentioned. Them fellers ain't no good farm-workin'. Ellis an' Chick gonna help now."

Effie went in, dodging an icicle from the roof. Lige stayed out, chewing an icicle. He gazed west dreamily across the snow glitter. Ellis and I scrooged lower in the last wet straw of the cow barn.

Ellis said, "If he breaks that Eighty, he'll run his dang plow right into the Buffalo Waller. We can't have it no more. We better go dig up the stuff we hid out last fall. That cutter might roll right in an' bust the muskit. Or the Gran'pap rifle. Or the Johnny Reb carbine. Or the grub we buried—but it's froze now. Chick, he'll ruin the Waller."

"Aw, mebbe he won't break the West Eighty. Mebbe he gits a sick horse or gits too lazy, come spring! Just wait an' see!"

But we felt pretty bad about the old Buffalo Wallow. There it was all summer long, and what a boy's hangout in a treeless land! Far in the unbroken West Eighty, and you couldn't see it from the section-line road. The Eighty was all virgin prairie, buffalo grass and bluestem and little wild roses. The Waller was the spot gouged out by untold generations of buffalo as they rubbed their itchy backs into the under-sand. Lige, the first settler here, told us that. Maybe forty feet across and six feet at the deepest below the grassy wild-flower margins. Under the banks we had dug out little tunnels to sit in from the sun and to store all the plunder we hooked from Lige and cowhands, but it was ours anyhow, for it was all the broken, useless stuff that nobody wanted. But the only playthings we ever saw. Two ancient six-shooters with neither hammers nor triggers, a double-barrel shotgun with the breech blown off and the Civil War musket that my dad had left me when he went off to Mexico and never came back. All else he left me was the Johnny Reb cap which he grabbed off one when he was a Yankee Colonel. And his picture with a sword and black whiskers. Then we had the big Kentucky rifle, so heavy I couldn't lift it, with a beautiful walnut stock inlaid with silver. It had a powder pan and a hammer for flints. But we had no flints, and the vent was rusted and a ramrod had been broken off in the muzzle maybe a century ago—nobody knew when. Effie said it had come down from her folks Back East.

Ellis and I hated Back East. Omaha was Back East. Out West was Californy and Colorada, but where we lived wasn't West. We would never, on any account, go Back East. New York was Back East, and we sure hated New York. Lige told us all about them New Yorkers. They all wore plug hats, and all the work they ever did was to walk up and down a big street, whirl canes and collect Intrust on Mortgages. Every November Effie bustled about, small, sharp-eyed and energetic, and warned us if Lige couldn't dig up Intrust for them plug-hat New Yorkers we'd lose house and home. We mustn't expect any winter boots till Lige paid that Intrust.

But about Thanksgiving we'd be taken to town on our annual adventure in the wagon and get our feet into new copper-toed boots. Town was the general store, dark and smelling of leather. There was a stock-loading chute, a grain elevator and two saloons—and mud, mud everywhere, soft mud or frozen mud. Either was tough when you had to stumble about in new boots. We hated boots as much as plug hats. Then we had to start school, two miles through deepening prairie snows, and boots never seemed warm or dry until spring, blessed spring. Then a boy could get rid of that agonizing struggle to get his boots on and off. But this last month of melting snow was the worst. By then your boots had holes in them and the icy water swelled your feet, and the day came when you cut the instep away to get the boots off and then could limp barefooted but in delight through the frosts of spring.

Then a boy could warm his feet by chasing one of the milk cows up and squatting in the spot where she had bedded. Sit on his feet in a little warm spot in the frosty grass.

Spring was fine also because then you quit school. Let the teacher holler; she couldn't catch you.

Effie would jaw some, but we would show a sudden vast interest in her new vegetable garden; and now also we had to ride fence and stretch barbed wire to keep the cows out of Lige's young corn. The range land was about gone, but some of the longhorns, thin and savage, would raid the fences. Lige said cows had busted him up, and if he knew which of them wild critters was his he'd go out and shoot them; but they weren't worth skinning. Ellis and I eagerly volunteered if he'd give us powder for the muskit, but he said we were too little to fool with them bad steers.

Our cowhand had faded away with the snows. We knew he'd be back after summer riding with some outfit. But we didn't know now that he'd gone until one of the boys at school who lived over south said that Earl had passed his place one morning, riding his pinto and dragging his pack animal along, with pots and pans clattering against his blanket roll. And swearing at his third cayuse, which was no good but wanted to tag along. Earl was in a hurry, for everywhere now he smelled new-plowed farm lands and it just made a cowhand weak, thinking of all that work.

He was the last cowhand I ever saw for years and years, until Hollywood started its stuff. That glamour word "cowboy" was rarely heard in our neighborhood, but when Ellis and I ever found Earl all duded up to go to town we'd yell it derisively at him. Earl would have clean denims tucked into plain black boots—no fancy-stitched rodeo tops; no pretty hanky around his neck, no beautiful white hat. He'd wear his town shirt, blue flannel with a big red rosette on the tobacco pocket; he'd be shaved so close that his jaws were blue, and he'd smell of Jockey Club perfume. Many a day we had hunted his bunk over and over, in the straw floor, in the pole chinks, for that stuff and never could find it. But any day we saw him duded up for town we'd run out to the road and yell, "Cowboy, cowboy, git to town an' git drunk! Git 'im a chippie an' git drunk! Cowboy! Cowboy!"

Earl would just grin, and when he came home some drunk he'd give us a dime to sneak grub out of the soddy without Effie knowing it. But she always did. Once I overheard her say to Lige, "Them boys been hookin' a drink outa Earl's bottle. Land, what next? I found Chick stealin' powder outa yore flask an' pourin' it in his bottle to take out to fight Indians in the Waller."

"Well, them boys growin' up. Got to have leetle powder fer their muskit. I miss caps an' buckshot too, but I don't say nothin'."

Good old Lige! Tall and lank, grizzled of chin and hairy-eared, lost in that dream of a big farm. Corn, wheat, oats, barley, buckwheat—anything except cow critters.

Effie, tiny and sharp-eyed, went on: "Well, you ain't got a cowhand any more, an' them boys got to ride fence an' battle off some mean ones. They get their legs cut on bobbed wire an' won't tell me about it. I just find their pants tore an' bloody. They's growin' up tough. They cuss now."

"Yeh, I guess. They better harden up. Let 'em cuss. I do."

"That teacher said they don't want to learn nothin'. Well, time I saw her I didn't figger she knew much, a hat like she had."

My fighting little aunt! I'd been dumped down on her hands, aged two, after my dad had gone off to Mexico or somewhere and died. My mother had died, and I had no memory of her. Effie was the only woman I knew. Effie and Teacher—but we dodged Teacher pretty well.

She boarded off south with the Germans, who had a frame house. Bad blizzard days they took her to school in a covered wagon with south-section boys and girls. Ellis and I got there somehow, on foot or riding the farm horses which were all we got to handle—Tops and Jewel, shaggy, gaunt and tired, but kind to small boys.

There were three other teams lazing around in the East Eighty timothy pasture—when they didn't push through the flimsy barbed wire strung to broken boards and cottonwood poles, for Lige couldn't get good posts. Then they gathered around the corn mountains, but with all their eating they didn't get fat. Just potbellied. But Tops and Jewel were our riding outfit. Some cold days Ellis and I rode them to school so they'd be handy if any of the range cattle strayed too near the ranch. Then we'd abandon school with a yell, run out and mount to turn back the invaders. Then back to the one-room frame schoolhouse where Teacher and the dozen "scholars" were

huddled about the potbelly stove. Twenty feet from it
the wooden water bucket had a never-thawing cover of
ice. You'd have to hammer this with the tin dipper to get
a drink. We didn't think this was bad; what was there to
holler about? I thought all boys and girls lived just as we
did—except them plug-hat New Yorkers. I couldn't imag-
ine how they lived, and didn't care.

Springtime school was better, but that's when you'd be
figuring to quit. With only a mile to the Buffalo Waller,
what for school? Teacher would have a time with recita-
tions. And of all learning Joggerfee was best. It came in
a wide thin book which a boy could erect on his desk and
Teacher couldn't see what he was doing. Behind the Joggerfee a boy could play with his snake, the little garter
snake he'd find by the rain-water pools in the prairie.
Open your Joggerfee to a map and your snake would start
crawling all over the United States until you steered it
back. Joggerfee consisted mostly in bounding the states—
of all the fool things to do! Teacher would say, "Chick,
bound Rhode Island."

"Uh—you mean the whole island or just the town on
the island?"

"Sit down and study your Geography again. Harry,
bound Connecticut."

Harry couldn't even pronounce it. But he had a good
defense. "That-there state is too little. On the map it's
just a little pink smear by a blue one. Chick, he busted
some eggs on my Joggerfee, an' . . . an' . . . well, I can't
find that-there state."

Teacher gave up and called on a girl. Girls could rattle

off learning at a great rate, not having to ride herd on snakes over their Joggerfee maps.

Well, with spring Ellis and I sneaked our few dirty books out of school and quit. This modern horror, homework, was unknown. Boys wouldn't have stood for it; learning was bad enough at best, and once out of that school it was totally out of mind.

From school Ellis and I headed across the prairie Eighty to the Waller. It was all a wavering grass carpet with the sweet little wild roses growing in clear water pools. Meadow larks called joyously. Red-winged blackbirds darted ahead. Over us long angles of ducks and geese were heading north. Spring was the time when Ellis and I tried our most earnest hunting. Quail and prairie chickens were all about us too, but the problem was to get enough powder and shot for the muzzle-loading muskit. Lige had a good double-barrel shotgun, but he never hunted. What for when we had all the meat we wanted? Game laws were unknown to us. Ellis and I poured powder down the muskit. And then we'd start a crawl along the young corn rows, through cold mud sloughs and weeds until dark, on the trail of millions of ducks. Wary, competent ducks who'd eye two wet boys trying to swing that long gun, longer than we were, in their direction, and then take wing with scornful clamor. We'd go home very wet and subdued.

It was a land of no Old Settlers whatever. No one except Uncle Lige had been there more than ten years. After the railroad came, the buffaloes and Indians vanished, and the trail herds no longer followed any route through this county. Our pioneers knew nothing, not even dim tales of any past. We were now the earliest ones and didn't know it.

But what freedom! What a life for boys! No doctoring, no preaching, examinations, Boy Scout routines, cheer leaders, yell leaders, coaches or advisers pleading with us to be better boys! No permits, licenses of any sort. Lige told us that Back East you had to have a card of some sort before you could go hunting. He said in New York if you wanted to shoot somebody you had to go to the sheriff and get a permit. I'd believe anything of plug-hat folks. I'd never seen a plug hat, but Lige had when he was in the Tennessee Army. He told us about Mortgages too and how we better all light out of here before a Mortgage got us.

Effie said not to believe Lige all the time. Well, we didn't. We didn't believe anybody much. We never confided in grownups and they didn't pay much attention to us. That was exactly the way we wanted it, and we never complained about anything, so they couldn't meddle. What a life! Freedom! Where is that freedom now for a boy in all America, the wise and troubled land?

Visiting was little done in that country. Jogging for hours in a wagon under western sun or in winter drifts kept women from gadding to neighbors. Once in a while some folks who had a baby came along and camped by our corral. This was terrible. Ellis and I fled to the Buffalo Waller and stayed there until the outfit with the baby jogged off. We wouldn't stay in earshot of one of those squallers. They smelled bad too. A baby was a kid. A boy was never called a kid unless you were pickin' on him for a fight. That was an insult, calling him kid. Ellis and I lived entirely to ourselves. We rarely saw another boy except at school, and that was where the fights started. I never could lick anybody, for I was the smallest and skinny at that. But I tried now and then. In fact I had to. The big boys, about fourteen and sixteen, came to school winter months only when there was little work at home. So they had the big fights in the deep snow back of the schoolhouse end where there were no windows, noon hours when we ate the pocket lunches brought from home. When the big boys wanted a change they'd make us smaller boys fight by shoving us into one another until somebody either got mad or realized that he wouldn't have any peace until he did whale away at the other boy's nose. So a boy had to fight one way or other. I never discovered what anyone was quarreling about before it reached the point of deep insult, and then at it we went.

When school was out Ellis and I waded off to the Buffalo Waller, our fortress and refuge and council chamber. Most of the scholars came from the south side, where there were more families, and we never went near their ranches if we could avoid it. Our north side was mainly unbroken prairie, and no other boys came that way except us. That would be a challenge to trouble.

Effie tried to make us believe that the reason for all the rows at school was because we had no manners. She said that when we met any folks we should shake hands and say "Thank you" or "Much obliged." It didn't do any good at school, but the habit stuck to me for years. Years later when I finally saw Back East folks and was scared of them, I used to mumble "Much obliged," hoping they wouldn't jump on me. It worked fine socially—mumbled.

Well, enough about culture. Ellis and I learned a deal from various cowhands who hung around Lige's the cold months and vanished in the spring, dodging farmwork like Earl did. Ellis and I missed cowhands some, for when they were about and came home pickled to snooze away in the straw bunk shed we would get the ca'tridges out of their guns. Out at the Waller we'd twist the bullets out, empty the powder into our whisky flask and fill the shell with sand. Then we'd crimp the bullets back in and take the ca'tridges back to shove into the victim's holster.

Then someday the rider would want practice on a post owl or jack rabbit. The percussion cap would snap and that's all. He'd try another and another, all six, and would he swear! At the man who sold him his ammunition. If these pore lads had ever taken a close look at their shells, they'd have seen the tampering. But they were too mad. They'd eject all the shells and ride on. Then Ellis and I would take their trail and pick up the shells too, for then we had the lead as well. Then we'd make slugs for the muskit by chopping and pounding bullets on an old piece of anvil iron at the Waller. We crammed the lead chunks down the muskit barrel on top of some grass wadding on the powder we'd hooked from Lige. Once I was dragging that heavy gun, longer than I was, back from the North Eighty, where Lige had sent me to chase the wild ducks off his first-breakin' fields. Ducks would ruin young sprouting corn. A mighty cloud of teal arose and went over me in the dusk. I couldn't shoulder the muskit, but I jammed the butt in the mud, pulled trigger and shut my eyes. Down came a bluewing. I yelled, grabbed it and raced to the soddy. Ellis wouldn't believe me. He'd never yet hit anything with the muskit. Effie wouldn't either. Said I couldn't aim that gun. The duck must have dropped dead with heart trouble, and she wouldn't cook it.

But the next day, out in the Waller where I roasted my duck on a ramrod over a grass fire, Ellis took a big chunk of it. But he wouldn't even taste baked snake. Lige said Indians ate snakes, and I thought, Then why couldn't we? But all I could taste was burned grass sticking to the snake's ribs—and a grasshopper fizzled to nothing but burned grass.

"Sure Indians eat 'em," said Ellis. "Not me!"

Indians were a constant topic for discussion.

Lige and Effie had started for Californy, but a horse had died and they'd squatted right here. Lived in their covered wagon that first winter until the sod house was built. Homesteaded and pre-empted and timber-claimed and bought until they had an entire half section of prairie for stock. Then Lige got the fool idea of farming: corn, wheat, oats, potatoes and everything he could plant. And then couldn't sell enough to keep Intrust going for them plug-hat New Yorkers. However, Lige had no idea of staying here. Californy for him. Pioneers around here had no plans except someday going somewhere else. Restless grinning Americans, following in after the Indians and buffaloes had vanished a decade ago. Foreign folks hoped to stay. Germans and Rooshins were just coming in.

Ellis and I listened to all this. But we didn't want to go to Californy. All you got there was gold. But if we could get to Colorada we'd fight Indians and climb mountains. Colorada was by far the best place.

But nobody went anywhere. Effie said, "What can't be cured must be endured. Who busted the top o' my cookstove? Now I have to hold the plate with a mess of bobbed wire on it. But what can't be cured must be endured. Git some hay twisted, Chick."

"Was you here when the Indians came hellin' down from Dakoty?"

"Never saw a fightin' Indian! It was just a lot o' fool talk by menfolks, but they all hit fer town and sat around drinkin' until they heard the Indians was headed west toward Colorada."

Colorada for us. I hoped the Indians would not be run out of Colorada till Ellis and I got there with the muskit. We'd saved nearly a pint of black powder off Earl and other cowhands who bunked with him a week maybe and came home drunk and then ate off Effie when they sobered. But we got some of their ammunition.

Earl hadn't been gone a week before his third mustang came back. It was a miserable outlaw pony that had never been ridden and nobody wanted, so likely he chased it from following him, and now, like all useless stuff, Ellis and I had a horse. A shaggy, mean-eyed, lop-eared sort of pony hanging around the rotted corn piles until he was potbellied. Cowpokes in those days were not romantics, nor heroic-minded. They'd think a man was loco who'd waste time trying to break an outlaw to ride.

Lige said to chase that critter away, but he had to eat. You couldn't lay hands on him either, but Ellis and I figured all spring how to break him. First catch him, of course. We laid lariats in loops around the corn pile, hid behind the corral posts and waited. For days he wouldn't step into our traps, and then one morning the fool actually jerked his mouth up full of fodder and the lariat went over his ears! We yelled and hauled, and the mustang bucked and leaped, jerking us into mudholes and out until that noose tightened and he fell over popeyed and half dead. We loosened the rope to give him a little breath and got a hobble on his forefeet. Ellis said, "Git yore saddle. It's no good anyhow if he starts to bust things up."

I got my saddle—another relic, with one broken stirrup, no pommel and no leather left on the seat. I rode a mess of splinters and old hairs rubbed off the various work horses we used. But now a cow pony, by golly! Getting that critter saddled was a half day's work. Effie would come to the soddy door and yell for corncobs, and Ellis would sneak away innocently so that she couldn't see what we were doing. I kept our pony choked close to the lariat pin, giving him a little air when he heaved too much.

We finally got that saddle over his bony spine and then, under back and belly, we got the cinch around him. Ellis slipped his old bridle over his ears. The pony opened his mouth to gasp and the bit went between his teeth when he was unconscious again. Ellis said, "Let the bugger git up. I'll hold the bridle while you climb on him."

"Who—me first?"

"Sure. It's yore saddle, ain't it?"

I got the hobble off his feet. Then the lariat loose from his neck. He heaved a mighty sigh and stood slowly up on tottering legs. Then the critter rolled the whites of his eyes at me. I put a hand on the saddle. It was going to be a climb with no stirrup. I reached for the reins. He seemed mad but controlling it. I got one hand to his shaggy hair. Then he started. I'd never heard of a rodeo, but this critter plainly knew the business. He bucked and spraddled, danced and wiggled. He rose on his hind legs, came down with a side swipe at me and then charged. Ellis went down, and the bridle slipped off. My cow pony swung and bucked once more. Then he started south, faster and faster, down the rutty road. Ellis said, "Now see what you gone an' done! Got yore saddle too."

"Lookit him go! Wish I was on him. Headed for Texas, I bet."

We couldn't see him now, and we never saw him again. Bound for Texas with a saddle on his back. I wondered what other wild horses would think when he joined up. I wondered how much rolling and scratching he'd do before he got that saddle off his back. I wondered if that crazy outlaw would hook into Earl's outfit again. Earl would sure be discouraged, the world against him.

Well, spring was here. Lige plowed his old fields and said nothing about the West Eighty. We had great hopes for our prairie.

One day he got out his rusty corn planter and was getting seed into the plowed North Eighty. Ellis and I had harrowed it willingly, because we hoped to keep the fool man so busy that he couldn't start on the prairie land. We became good boys, cleaning the dilapidated horse barn and yard, burning off the dead weeds and grass from the sod-house roof so it would grow green again in summer. Going out to Lige's field and talking. Following him around, talking, anything to delay him, drag his spring work out so that it would be too late to plow the last prairie around the Buffalo Waller. Upset his mind, that's what. And I began to figure how to upset him.

I said to Ellis, "Looky, nobody ever dies or gets killed around here. But suppose we find a dead feller off somewhere an' just whisper it ain't nothin' to talk about. Get Lige worried."

"How we find a dead feller?"

"That's the mystery. We just hint mebbe he's murdered."

"But we ain't got any dead feller."

"Well, I got to consider somethin'. Start a mystery. We got to get Lige's mind off breakin' up the West Eighty prairie."

I went off to the windbreak. The cottonwoods were so small that, when I'd rigged some pieces of rope for a swing between the two biggest ones, their tops bent over and my feet hit the ground. Always I went out there when I had to consider something. Ellis didn't understand how I was considering. He was a fat, cautious boy with freckles, and he jeered at my swing because he couldn't get into it without his bottom hitting the ground. "Just like a dang girl, swingin'. What you see when you swing up?"

"Clouds. Big, like pictures o' mountains. Out West clouds." I kicked to the top of the swing. Prairie clouds were beautiful. It was the first time in my life that I'd thought of beauty. But I didn't dare say so.

Ellis jeered on: "You read too much. I mean in that newspaper Lige got last month. Always got yore nose into big words. But we don't want no books."

"Yeh, I guess. School reader's bad enough. But I want to get an idea how to stop Lige breakin' the prairie."

Ellis thought of something else. "Say, that wagonman camped back o' the corral, he's got a dog with no tail. He says it's stylish. What he calls a screw-tail terrier. He told me how to fix all our pups stylish with screw tails. Want to try it?"

"Sure. Chop their tails off while they're little."

"Naw, that's no good! Then you got just a ord'nary bobtailed hound. He says, to get screw tails on a dog you got to chaw their tails off. Bite with a kinda twisty jerk to make a screw tail. Want to try it?"

Well, that took my mind off Lige and how to find a dead feller, maybe murdered, and get folks excited. So I said, "Sure. We'll take the best pup out to the Waller an' fix him a screw tail. We got eight pups now an' ought to have one of 'em stylish. We'll surprise Effie."

Ellis said, "We got to go out there and give the Buffalo Waller a spring house cleanin' like Effie's doin' the soddy. Stuff we stowed there last fall's all rotten now. An' now snow's gone that dang dead cow's got her hoofs up again. She don't smell so bad as she did; her hide's sinkin in, all dried up. But what we got to do is bury her again before rains come."

Ellis looked at me cautious-like, and I knew what he meant. He always wanted me to take the lead in anything that might not pan out. I was the one who had to hook something out of the soddy that we wanted at the Waller, while Ellis kept his ma interested in her vegetable garden, pretending, maybe, that he'd found a new bug on the tomaters.

So we went out and tackled the dugout under the side of the Buffalo Waller, put new sod on the roof and raked the dirt floor.

That cow had been a problem all last summer. The winter before she'd blizzard-drifted into our fortress, died and been invisible until the snow melted. We couldn't drag her out, so we tried to bury her. Dug with hands and sticks down under her for weeks, and she swelled and smelled worse every week. We got her under the sand, but every time a big rain fell a hoof or a horn would show up. Finally we gave up and played she was a buffalo. We thumped gumweed arrows into her dried hide and hung the powder horn on her own wide ones. The second summer she didn't smell so bad, but Effie complained that we still did when we came home. Our dogs roamed far to dine on dead cattle after the snow vanished, and between dogs and boys Effie was in a state o' mind, she said. Said she was going to tame a skunk to even on us.

We carried the best pup out to the Buffalo Waller the next morning. A glorious prairie morning of waving grass in cold rain-water pools, red-winged blackbirds swinging on the reeds, and the little wild roses which ranged thick around the margin of the Waller, smelling very sweet in triumph over the cow down in the lowest sand hollow. Across our last prairie, faint and far we heard Lige's checkrower. It would be no good at all on first breakin', and this was late spring. Maybe we had Lige licked. First-breakin corn had to be hand-planted.

The pup seemed suspicious when I straddled him and straightened his tail out for Ellis. The wagonman said if you bit quick it was easy, the bones being so tender. Ellis was suspicious too, and I yelled for him to chaw quick before the pup squirmed. So he took the first bite. The pup yelled some. And Ellis quit and told me to calm him down. "You, Chick, make him stop squirmin'. Wait now——"

"You're scared," I yelled. "Watch me!"

"Give it a kind o' twisty chaw like the man said to get a good screw tail on him," Ellis said. "Twisty-like."

I took a good deep chaw, my mouth full of hair. The pup screamed murder, fought from under my legs and headed home. Ellis gazed anxiously. "Just hear him yelp! Where's his tail, then?"

"I dunno. Mebbe I swallered it. I tasted hair or somethin'."

"You're a dang liar! He's wavin' his tail right now!"

When the pup saw me again he went to a gopher hole, stuck his tail in it and sat on it. He grew to be a fine hound-dog, but he never trusted me again. The covered-wagon man had hitched and gone after eating with us for a week. No pay. Strangers came rarely, and Lige was glad to talk with a man. Food didn't figure. There was so much, as Lige kept on creating it and couldn't sell for enough to pay a day's hauling.

Food? I didn't believe that anybody in the world could ever go hungry. I thought everybody lived as we did. In spring Ellis and I had to shovel out rotted food from the sod-banked holes under the snow. Potatoes, turnips, cabbage; and the corn and wheat piles now were green little mountains. The cows and pigs and chickens didn't want it when there was green young spring grass. And the poor dogs and cats—all they had to eat was beefsteak, pork ribs,

side meat, liver, sody biscuit, corn bread, fried eggs—
everything we had. What a life for dogs and boys! So
many eggs in summer that Ellis and I threw them at knot-
holes, cats and each other. Sick of hard-boiled eggs at
school. Food—and Lige, the locoed farmer, kept on raising more!

Sweating and grinning, he hefted me one day and said
I must weigh near a hundred pounds now. Ellis said that
was a bad sign. Lige was going to wrangle us into some
kind of field work. We'd try—if only we wouldn't start
first-breakin' the last prairie. Maybe he'd clean forget
it now.

Spring was warming up. We'd worked more than
boys should, trying to distract Lige from the last prairie.
Bumblebees were building tough papery nests in the sod,
and we flagged 'em and jugged 'em. Flagging meant pulling a pole off the straw barn with a rag tied to the end.
Punch the nest, and out the big black-and-yellow fellers
boiled. They lit into the rag, and you rolled 'em up and
then stamped it. Jugging was good on a windy day. You
set the jug, half filled with water, near the nest, kicked it
hard and ran. Out came the bees, and, hearing the wind
roar in the jug, they dived into it—and the water. When
we safely could pull the nest away we ate the thick black
honey—and maybe a grub or so.

Sometimes a boy got stung pretty badly. Bee stings
weren't so bad as the summer sores we acquired on our
legs. Dust or burs or something would start them, and
they wouldn't heal until cool fall weather. It wasn't fair
rasslin' to kick a boy on the shins. Far as might be, we
kept our sores from Effie's sight. She'd brew Spanish-

needle tea, and that was terrible stuff to take. We'd manage to spill most of it outside our mouths, not in, and she wouldn't notice. There were only two medicines in the soddy: Carbolic Acid Salve and Piso's Pain Killer for Consumption. Killer was pretty good, tasting like Earl's whisky, but a boy couldn't work a swig of it from Effie's trunk.

That little wooden trunk, horsehair-covered, held all the culture that Effie had fetched from Back East, and which we boys had no curiosity about. But stuff that tasted like whisky was something else. Good for belly-ache, but no use trying to make Effie believe we had bellyaches or even consumption. She said we were too tough to get sick. When Ellis or I got a loose tooth she tied a string about it and the other end to the door and said, "Just slam that door shut an' out comes the tooth."

This provoked rebellion. It hurt even to give the string a little jiggle. So we would wear the pieces of string around hanging from our mouths for days, experimenting with the pain. If Lige or Earl, the cowhand who stayed winters with us looking after the little stock left on our vanishing range, got hold of that string, he'd yank and we'd yell, but out came the tooth, and Lige would give us a chew of plug tobacco to heal the hole. Then we had something to show at school when we had to go back, the toothache excuse now no good to tell Effie.

Effie was always telling us how well off we were, and on the Joggerfee map she'd point out the lands where boys didn't get enough to eat, so she'd heard Back East. We ought to be thankful things were so fine with us. "All the food we raise an' waste because we can't sell it! And if

Lige doesn't scrape up enough money fer the Mortgage next fall, you boys won't eat either mebbe!"

Of course we didn't believe her about Chinee boys not having enough to eat. If it was summer with all the hens "laying out," we just started another egg battle.

An early dry spell came, and young corn shriveled. Then a black dust storm came from southwest from what the Joggerfee map named the Great American Desert. The wind blew Lige's young wheat out of his fields and scattered it into his corn, into the road ruts, everywhere except where he'd sowed it. Ellis and I were delighted. Now he'd never have time to plow up the Buffalo Waller prairie. Lige just grinned; had too durn much grain planted anyway. Effie said, "Well, how about Intrust fer the Mortgage next November? An' you boys won't get boots fer school either."

Well, that was fine and far off. Ellis dug up the three dimes we had buried at the Waller which cowpokes had bribed us with to get something to eat from the soddy and decided to give them toward Intrust when disaster came. When full summer came we felt pretty safe about the ol' Waller. So we didn't work so much to please folks. Effie was trying to raise some Back East flowers in the vegetable garden, but they weren't pretty as wild roses in spring rain-water pools. One of the reasons Lige gave for never getting to Californy was that Effie wouldn't move on after she saw prairie roses, and Effie would kind of blush on her brown face and say it was just a fib—but I saw she was pleased.

One day Ellis ran to the big ragweeds where I was watching little chickens hatch out and yelled, "Now he's

done it! Got his plow in West Eighty prairie! Do somethin', Chick!"

"Look, yore always tryin' to git me to try somethin' you
don't wanna tackle. Like the pup's tail an' ridin' that
mustang. If I'd got on him, I'd be in Texas right now!"

"Texas just a lot o' dang cows! You run out an' stop
Lige so he don't ruin the Waller! He's doin it!"

"Well, the ol' coot fooled us. Ain't said a word fer
weeks about any first breakin' on the prairie. Now he's
started."

"We better do somethin' quick, the ol' son of a gun!"

We went out beyond the windbreak and stared west.
There at our feet began that cursed furrow straight out
through the virgin prairie. A beautiful, first-breakin' furrow black and steady as far as we could see in the grass.
Not a clod in it, just a long black ribbon held firm by the
upturned grass roots. The tough sod which had never been
stirred in all its years under the sun and snows. Ellis and I
turned away discouraged. Out there the old Buffalo Waller,
and we couldn't save it any more than we could the last
prairie!

Lige and his team were so far we could see only their
backs above the summer grasses. The pink wild roses of
spring were gone. There were no cool, clear little sloughs
now with the plovers and blackbirds darting. But a meadow lark still called, and a striped gopher frolicked—but
they wouldn't for long out there. They wouldn't have
the ancient home now. They wouldn't stay on the muddy
cornfield places. When the prairie went they would go too.

Ellis and I didn't talk any more. We felt pretty tough.
It took a long time for the first-breakin' team to round a

"land" and come back. We sat by the start of the furrow in silence. Then we heard the distant clank of trace chains. Then the panting of the team, and then the smooth hiss of the rollin'-cutter slicing the sod ahead of the plowshare. We peered above the grass. I saw Jewel's ears now, and then Lige's old gray hat. Then the lines over his shoulders and his sweating face. He came slowly on along his first furrow. I had to roll aside from Jewel's feet, and Ellis stood up with a green buffalo pea in his mouth which was puckering strangely.

Ellis couldn't speak. Lige must have seen that, for he addressed himself to me. "Hi, young feller! Look at my furrow o' first breakin'. Ever see such a furrow? Goes half a mile without a break in the sod—now that's ol' tough prairie, ain't it?"

"Yeh," I said sulkily. "I guess."

"Soon's I let the team blow an' git a drink, you boys come out with me. I bet, Chick, you never saw such good first breakin' before."

I wouldn't answer. Ellis looked the other way toward the soddy. We could hear the gurgle of water down Lige's gullet. Then he grinned again. How could he be so cheerful, all sweaty-like, and like a man who's done a good deed?

We wouldn't talk to him, but when he said "Giddap!" and started his plow on the second furrow we followed along, our toes in the smooth black bottom of it. On and on went Lige and Jewel and Old Tops. On and on, with Ellis staring coldly, a rod back of his pa's hands on the plow handles.

"Too late now," I whispered over Ellis' shoulder. "This

time he'll go whack right into the Waller. Mebbe we got time to yank the muskit an' the Kentucky gun out from the hole all wropped in the ol' blanket. Mebbe we—— Hey, now, he's turnin'!"

"Gee!" Lige cried. "An' whoa, now, you critters! Rest a spell."

We ran around the outfit and stared. The plow hadn't gone within sixty feet of the Buffalo Waller. Lige had come up and made a skirl, and his black furrow went away off left to the section line and made its turn. "Doggone!" Ellis was running for the Waller. He jumped down into it. I could just see his freckled ears. He was yelling—I don't know what.

I started that way too, and Lige called me back. "Look now, Chick, when I got up here on that first furrow Jewel quit. Tops too!"

"What you mean? They wouldn't plow the Waller?" I muttered.

"No-sir-bobbee, they just balked. First time Ol' Tops ever balked on me. Plumb mystery."

I wouldn't answer such foolishness. Ellis was wiping his nose. We glared at that little rolling wheel ahead of the plowshare. It was worse than any Indians we'd have to fight off the Waller. Old Tops was looking around at Lige and then at me. Many a hot day I'd kicked bare heels into his bony ribs riding fence, playing each rickety post was an Indian warrior and had to be whacked as my steed passed.

Lige kept on grinning. "Only way I can figger is that these critters balked on me because they knew you boys loved this ol' hole in the prairie. They just went off geeing

around it. They left mebbe a whole acre o' prairie around
it too—for you. Git your guns an' play shootin' ag'in.''

He slapped the reins on Jewel's back. "Giddap!" And
off the team went into the prairie to the left. We heard the
panting horses, the clank of traces and the slither of the
cutter in the tough sod. Fainter and fainter, and then it
died out toward the house. Ellis said, "Dang it, what got
into Lige tellin' us that?"

"We did! The cuss never figgered to break our prairie!
He just tickled himself by scarin' us all spring, an' now
blamin' Tops an' Jewel for it. Come on, let's run home an'
holler! To Effie an' the whole blame ranch let's holler! I
bet Effie made Lige do this!"

Ellis dropped the muskit in the Waller and we ran. Ran
and yelled back along Lige's first furrow. What a beautiful first-breakin' furrow, black solid ribbon through the
prairie grass! We burst into the soddy yelling.

"You know what? Lige left us a whole acre of prairie!
Fer Chick an' me!" Ellis cried.

"Ain't goin' to be plowed not ever forever, by anybody!"

Effie's small sun-leathered face had a rare sweet smile. "It
sure won't be as long as I have a say about this land. Last
prairie belongs to you boys. Now run, git your guns."

"Yeh," I blurted. "But you oughta heard what we
called Lige when we first saw that breakin'. I said he was
an ol' coot."

"I said he was a reg'lar son of a gun!" Ellis yelled.

"I cussed in them Pawnee words, which is awful. We
thought he'd just made us suffer all spring, thinkin' he'd
start first breakin' and then hopin' he wouldn't."

"We wouldn't have worked so hard draggin' the North Eighty an' cleanin' up the place except we was hopin'. Mebbe we oughta run out there an' 'pollergize—what you call it."

"No." Effie was laughing. "Just go on bein' pretty good boys. Land, I forgot my bread sponge a-settin' too long! Git some cookies an' run. An' who stole that crock o' buttermilk I was coolin' in the windmill tank?"

We didn't answer. We fled yelling out through the virgin prairie of the West Eighty. Meadow larks rose singing sweetly. Red-winged blackbirds teetered on the slough grass. Spring roses were gone, but now you could eat the dried buds for chewin' tobacco. I was ahead because Ellis was too fat. I heard him pant.

"You heard? Waller ain't ever goin' to be plowed, not ever!"

"Not ever! Not by nobody, forever an' ever!"

# 3

## Where Is That Land?

**W**E LOST. Nearly seventy years later Ellis drove me out a fine road lined with box elders. I had not seen him for fifty years. The car purred past the long-abandoned schoolhouse, now a ruin. Busses came along here now to pick up country "kids." A fine tame land.

Ellis stopped at a section corner and pointed. "That's where the soddy was. Home."

I was silent. Nothing there except corn. Not a windbreak tree, windmill, stick of fence or soddy or corral. Not a sign that boys had ever played here, nor grownups worked and laughed and dreamed at this spot. Corn, bright blades and waving tassels. Food—mighty corn!

Ellis said, "After Lige died at sixty-nine Effie and me moved to town. I got some school. You'd gone off to be a newspaperman in Californy and places. I got to be rural-mail carrier and retired after thirty years. Now I'm eighty and never in bed sick yet. How're you?"

"Never sick in my life. That old West must have made us tough buggers. Well, I don't want to see this. Show me the Waller."

Ellis went on as if not hearing. "Now I know that first winter—'69—the folks livin' in that covered wagon, it must have been bad. But I never heard 'em complain about a thing. Cheerful folks. And Lige never got to Californy

45

with all his talk. Never got forty miles from his land in forty years. Wound up in Farmers' Valley buryin' ground. But Effie saw Californy! First war boom she sold the section at two hundred an acre. But she didn't like Californy. Came back to sleep with Lige again. At ninety-six years she weighed just ninety-six pounds. Pound each for every fightin' year she lived. Chick, you and me retired, but they never retired. Battled this land to the end of their days."

"Old-timers made a pretty country, but I don't want it now. Show me the Buffalo Waller."

At the west section line he pointed. "See it?"

I looked above the whispering corn. At last I made out a slight depression in the level field. Ellis said, "The big company tractors can fill a hole. I carried mail this route while Effie lived in town. I never told her what was goin' on out here. When she sold she tried to fix it so our prairie'd never be broke. Said the last acre belonged to the boys. I let her dream on, but somebody told her at last."

A school bus was passing, swiftly cheerful. Ellis grinned. "Pretty soft for kids now, isn't it? Would you swap with 'em?"

"No! Well, let's get back to town. Pretty country . . . but . . . "

"I know how you feel. Now you seen it, I'll never drive this road again. You ought to have seen Effie last time she went into the bank and bawled the land company out about breakin' that last prairie acre. Passed ninety, an' she cussed 'em. But couldn't save it." Ellis laughed. "She told 'em they was worse 'n a bunch o' plug-hat New Yorkers."

I got to thinking as Ellis drove back. A pretty country.

Nice and tame, hauling kids to school, all vaccinated and lunch-dieted likely. I thought a bit and began laughing. "Say, Ellis! We used to think we were fooling Lige and Effie, keeping all our troubles from them, but they knew all the time——and never interfered."

"That was the big thing. Freedom! But we were mighty conceited boys. And ignorant of the world."

"That was a big thing too. So it never worried us. World, eh? Just look at it now!"

Ellis laughed. "Boys—or, as we say, kids now—couldn't know that freedom. What we had is lost forever. Television, radio, talking pictures, comics, daily papers, all advisin' us what to do."

"We live in the Age of Advice. How to act, how to eat, how to look—oil on your hair and shiny white teeth—all as advertised. Editors, columnists, commentators—everyone telling everybody else what to do. Dammit! Magazines tell boys and girls how they must smell. Dogs too. Don't do this and don't do that. Propaganda—we never heard of any. We had freedom of a sort that a boy today couldn't find anywhere."

"That life and land have vanished, and I guess that kind of people too." Ellis was laughing again. "Where could a boy live with a woman like my mother?"

Little old tough-bodied, tough-minded Effie! Pioneer woman of the prairies. Long as she could, fighting for the last acre of unbroken sod to keep it for the meadow larks and striped gophers and black-and-yellow bumblebees—and boys. Symbol of a lost land. Now, in all the perplexed world of permits and truant laws, of road patrols and wardens, of registrations and ideologies, where could a boy find it? He doesn't know it ever existed.

# 4

# We Discover a Mighty River
# (South Road)

---

### I.

**B**UT LET's go back long years to a vanished life, a lost land.

The first folks who came into our prairie country had heard a lot about Western cyclones. Some, like Uncle Lige, dug a hole before they even broke sod for a house. Lige was a worse scary man about those twisters than anyone else we knew.

Any little black patch in the big summer thunderheads would have him gazing anxiously at the sky, then back to his cyclone hole, as if calculating how long it would take him to run there if the blow hit. If it seemed too close, he'd unhitch and come in from his fields nearer the ranch just in case. This made Effie laugh, and we boys followed her derisive line. Lige was full of dire warnings that sometime we'd be sorry.

One morning, muggy and windless, Ellis and I were out at the section-line corner where the Four Roads met. We had the tattered Joggerfee map, and we were in our usual debate over where the roads led if you only went far enough. Brown autumn grass was so high where the hidden roads crossed that you couldn't see the exact center

**48**

of America, but the surveyors' iron stake was there. We got deep in the endless discussion and hardly glanced at a long storm front building up in the west.

Ellis said, "South Road first. That's the only one marked right across the map, up an' down, an' it winds up in the ocean. Let's start early tomorry. Ocean's too far, but we can explore a piece."

"Go as far as we can an' look around. Never been far south beyond Gebauer's. It's all prairie beyond that."

I looked up. We lived in a world of light. In winters the mighty snowdrifts covered the Four Roads of Mystery, glittering in the sun. We struggled over and through them to arrive sometime or other at the half-buried schoolhouse, our eyes narrowed behind Effie's big home-knit mufflers. Then we sat, half-blinded, a long time about the little coal stove until we could make out the dizzy words in Second Reader. Teacher had the only coal around there by mid-winter. School out, we went again into the intolerable glitter homeward. In summer the vast light was a blue dome, the cloud banks rising in huge shining battlements over the treeless sky rim, but this white was not the winter-cruel which blinded me for Second Reader. I knew that stuff anyway.

Under the mighty eternal light we lived our small inter-esting lives, penned to the earth but staring up. The next intimations of beauty I knew were when I looked into the vastness of cloud and sky. I was staring now when Ellis said, "Hey, Lige is unhitched an' back at the corral close to his cyclone hole. That is a bad-lookin' cloud now!"

I said, "Well, I ain't goin' to run till Effie runs. Any-how, I want to see a dang twister close up so it scares me."

The whole west was magnificent with storm. White clouds were reaching far over us, and below them a black-green streak moving fast. The bottom of it was beginning to twist.

"Come on," Ellis yelled. "That's a twister all right!"

Wind began to scurry the dried grass. When we neared the house I could hear Lige yelling, "Hole up, quick! She's a buster!"

Effie stood in the sod-house door, waving a spoon.

I said, "She ain't excited. She's fryin' fried cakes. I ain't goin' to run till Effie runs."

That green-black cloud had lowered its writhing end. Whirlpools of wind hit us. A chicken went skittering high over the soddy, screaming protests. The horses in the corral were looking disturbed. The milk cows in east pasture were starting for home.

I could hear Lige again. "Chick, you dang smarty, git down in the hole!"

"I ain't goin' to run till Effie runs."

He raised his voice, standing near his hole. "Effie, drap that cookin' an' run fer the hole!"

Effie waved her spoon and looked at the cyclone. "If that thing hits here, I won't have a tomater left to can!"

"Tomaters! Tomaters! You won't have roof over yore durn fried cakes, nor a windmill, nor a cow critter to milk! Here, you—Ellis! Mind yore pa for once. Git in the hole!"

Ellis didn't know what to do. He didn't want to run until I ran; and I wouldn't run until Effie ran. And I was scared too. Lige stood with one foot on the edge of his hole and the other foot on the sod. Nobody would ever go into his cyclone hole, not even a chicken. Effie would look in the dang thing and just laugh. Now she had gone back to her stove, fryin' fried cakes.

So Ellis and I didn't know what next. That cloud was coming fast and bad. Then I looked at Lige, and he did a funny thing—pulled his foot away from the hole and danced up and down. The dogs were making a terrible fuss. Stealer, now a young hound, was with them until he saw me. Then he sat down and inspected his tail. He recalled that I was the boy who tried to bite it off when he was a pup.

"What ails Pa now?" Ellis said. "Why don't he get in his hole if he's skairt?"

Effie heard the five dogs and came out. She gave one look at the cyclone and then at Lige, one foot down in the hole and the other out kicking at crazy dogs. I came closer and saw his whiskers waggle in the dust. Then I heard him: "Skunk!"

Ellis turned and yelled at Effie, "Skunk! In his hole!"

I yelled, "Cyclone comin' an' skunk in his hole!"

Wind and dust were so strong I could hardly hear Lige. I heard Effie: "If that man fools with a polecat, I won't let him in the house fer a week. You boys too. Stay away from that hole!"

Now, that cyclone hole was about five feet deep and six across, with some boards and sod over the top. If a cyclone came, it would tear everything up above ground. Folks in a hole could scrooge down even if the roof went off. But four of us and eight cats and five dogs would fill that hole up tight, and no room for a durn skunk even if he'd act decent.

Well, Effie went back to her stove. So I wouldn't run.

I watched the windmill. I wanted to see a windmill go
sailing up in the air. Ellis backed away from the hole, and
the dogs all came around me, plumb crazy, like they always
did in a skunk fight. I always had to go first and chunk
something at the skunk, upset him so the dogs could grab
hold and shake before they got too sick. Ellis always
egged me on to go first, for he said he got skairt in his
stomach. Effie was the one who always howled if me and
the dogs went fighting a skunk out on the prairie. But I
wasn't going down into any cyclone hole to chase any
skunk. Lige was humped in the door of his hole, but he
daren't go down. The twister was roaring right above us
now, it seemed, and I was scared. I wanted Effie to run
first, but she was back in the soddy cooking again.

So I just stood watching the thing. Dust was so thick
I couldn't see the cows any more. They began to bawl
like baby kids. The younger work horses milled around
in the corral. Ol' Tops, my saddle nag, who was retired
now, being the only animal left of the team with which
Lige had started for Californy, came to the fence and stuck
his nose on my shoulder. Well, if Effie wasn't scared and
Tops wasn't scared, I wouldn't run, but I was sure scared.

Effie came out again, her apron over her head, her hair
streaking out, and waved the fry spoon. "That twister's
spinnin' off north towards Dakoty. Chick, git some cobs
fer my stove."

Lige slowly lifted his foot away from his cyclone hole.
Sure enough, the thing was heading north now. Effie said,
"Go away an' that skunk'll come out an' go about his business come night. Anybody gits skunk smell on him can't
come in an' eat."

The skunk did smell excited now.  Lige went back to his plow team, shaking his head.  Ellis and I tried to call the dogs away, for if they smelled of the skunk and piled in on us tonight under the old covered wagon, as usual, we'd smell of skunk and couldn't go into the house to eat.  The skunk wouldn't come out, having no mind to go sailing to Dakoty chased by Lige and a windmill.

Well, Ellis got the cows in and milked at choretime, and I swilled the pigs.  We smelled just a little, enough so we ate supper outdoors, and the last thing before dark Effie hollered, "I smell you right now!  Don't git any breakfast tomorry if you go near that skunk!"

2.

Earl was with us again to hole up for the winter.  No wages from Lige, but he might help with the chores. Maybe.

So we decided to take the next day to explore South Road which, in the Joggerfee, leads you to the ocean if you follow that line on the map far enough, as anybody can see.

Ellis and I crawled under the hay and pulled the old blanket over our heads to keep off mosquitoes.

Earl had gone down to Gebauer's and wasn't back yet. This German man hadn't been here but three years, but he had the finest house around.  Two stories and painted white.  You could see it far away on the prairie.  He had a good barn and fields fenced with good barbed wire.  I couldn't understand how a man who couldn't talk much English could ever get rich like that.  None of the Amer-

icans had paint on their houses. Effie declared again that
it was because we were too shiftless, always thinking of
pulling up stakes and drifting on somewhere else. Americans always seemed to live in sod houses and had fences
like Lige's, rusty pieced-out wire and busted boards and
cottonwood poles for posts, and a steer would just poke
his head through and push, and the whole dang fence
would come down. Ellis and I had the job of riding fence
with the wire stretcher and staples and fixing the fence
again. If the stock got into the young corn, Lige would
just swear and grin and maybe replant, maybe not.

Lige had been a West Virginia coal miner before he
came west and never had farmed land. He leaned on Earl
for advice, but Earl didn't know anything except cows.
Earl was from Arkansaw and had no homefolks, Effie said.
But he could write pretty good and figger, and Lige
couldn't. I guess he never got past Second Reader and
just grinned about it. Effie had been to school a lot or she
never could have read what was in her storybook about the
earl when knights were bold, as she told us. Our Earl was
still sad about cow business. His friend Marion Marlow,
who'd been on the Chisholm Trail once with Earl, hadn't
shown up yet to live on some kinfolks as usual until spring
cow business came on. Earl said this young hand, who was
all the time riding and drinking and shooting at jack rabbits and laughing, would get in trouble with the farmers
someday, cutting up like he did. Earl gave him good advice, but he was all the time worried about what Marion
would do next up here.

Well, this night the soddy was dark and Ellis and I almost asleep out under the wagon. I was wondering if I

smelled of skunk bad enough so I had to soap off by the windmill tank before I could go in for breakfast. It wasn't time for a bath for a long while yet.

Then I heard a funny creaking noise out on the road and then wheels. Then I heard Mr. Gebauer talking German, getting home so late from town that I crawled out to look. There he sat in the first buggy that ever was seen around our parts. The proudest man you ever saw. He stopped and lifted a lantern. Ellis crawled out by me. That buggy was just like pictures of them, all black and shiny and fine, but looked pretty rickety for prairie travel. Gebauer saw us and lifted a fine red whip with a tassel. Then he lifted his lantern higher so we saw somebody with him. He said, "Yah, see dot? Frawleen Westenhoffer from Old Country!"

"Miss Worsenever," I said, "much obliged."

We looked at her cautiously. She was taller than Gebauer and looked pretty good in front with blue eyes and pink cheeks, and she just smiled. Gebauer went on: "Yah! School—you see!"

Miss Frawleen Worsenever didn't say a word, not knowing enough.

Then some rider came into the lantern light and yelled, "Where's that triflin' no-good son of a gun Earl?"

It was Marion Marlow, but we were too locoed to answer. He was a sight. His cow pony jingled all over when it moved. Marion wore wide leather pants with big shiny buttons down the sides. He wore a short jacket with more buttons and red-and-yellow braid on it. He had a wide white hat, and it had fancy stuff all around it. His six-shooter was in a big leather holster with silver on it, and hooked to his saddle was a fancy leather lasso. Well, sir, nobody around there ever saw an outfit like that, just glittering all over, spurs to hat.

Marion roared, "Bring Earl out! Wanta have him see me!"

"He won't want to see you. No folks around here will! All duded up like that!"

"I been down in Mexico. This is a vaquero outfit. Git the folks out o' bed. I want everybody to see me!"

Gebauer cracked his shiny whip over his buggy nag. He yelled something again in German and started on. Miss Worsenever looked back and laughed. Couldn't talk. Just plumb ignorant.

Marion Marlow leaned over me before he followed. "That's Gebauer's niece, just emigratin' in an' goin' to live at his place an' go to school!"

"You're crazy! Anybody can't talk English is just plumb too ignorant fer even school." Ellis got excited. "If that longlegs goes to school, I ain't goin'!"

"Me either. Is she goin' to school in a buggy?"

Marion began laughing and spurred on. The whole outfit went on down South Road until all I saw was the lantern jogging up and down.

Before we could get back into the hay ol' Lige came to the door of the soddy. "What'n hell's goin' on out there? It's past nine o'clock."

"Mr. Gebauer's got a buggy. He's got a long-legged woman who's goin' to school. That settles it fer me. Chick an' me ain't goin'."

Effie stuck her head out. "Wasn't that Marion Marlow's voice?"

"Yeh, braggin' as usual. Been in Mexico an' says now he's a buckaroo. Dressed up like a Mexican, the dangest you ever saw."

"What's he doin', comin' from town with Gebauer?"

"Chasin' after that Miss Frawleen Worsenever, I guess. Earl's down South Road too. Did he know this long-legged girl was comin'?"

"Mebbe so. I heard a girl was comin', an' I egged Earl to go see her right away. But Marion came home with her first!" Effie was excited.

"Mebbe them two danged cowhands git in a fight about her."

Effie was more excited. "Sure! Two fellers an' a girl! Just like in my book!"

"Don't start on that book. If it says some feller couldn't live without her, it ain't nothin' to tell Earl. He knows a dang sight better. Earl ain't clean crazy enough to say that."

### 3.

It was before dawn when we got out of the hay and started on South Road, which ended in the ocean on the map.

We passed the Gebauer place at sunrise but a long way to the east from the road, for we didn't want to get any nearer that big girl we called Miss Worsenever, if she was going to school. But how could she if she didn't know much as I did, me in Second Reader? Two miles south in the dried September grass we found a big gully and followed along the bottom. It got deeper, and Ellis stared up the side. "Say, I bet that's like a hill!"

We'd never seen a hill, but we knew it was like one. Two miles on in this widening little valley we made a turn and then saw a dark smudge at the end of it. What could that be? It was midmorning when we were close enough to find out. Trees! Not like the trees at the ranches, all laid out in straight lines and about ten feet high for windbreaks. We went yelling under these strange trees and stared up. All a green tangle, and you could hardly see the sky. Big vines hung from them with black fruit, and I wanted to eat some. I said they were sure wild grapes. But Ellis hollered maybe they were the poison stuff that Indians put on arrowheads, and don't touch 'em. I ate one when he wasn't looking, and it didn't hurt me a bit. I'd seen pictures of grapes somewhere on an old box Lige fetched from town once. But we didn't eat any. We just went on staring up incredulously at the wonder of trees so big they hid the sky.

Ellis yelled, "Come on, Chick! I bet we find somethin' big in this new kind o' country. We got somethin' to tell folks!"

"I bet so! Look at the little round stones on the ground thick!"

We'd never seen the like. I broke through some big brush and then stopped quick. It was unbelievable, what I'd discovered. Yesterday was big enough, what with a cyclone and a skunk and Mr. Gebauer's buggy and that long-legged lady from Old Country and then Marion Marlow riding in dressed fit to kill. But this was bigger.

There at our feet was the great river that led to the ocean! We stood on the unknown pebbles and looked across flowing water. The sunlight glinted into a pool in a bend, and autumn leaves floated by. We saw little things darting in the water above the pebbles—could they be fish? I'd never seen fish even in a can. The morning was hot and still. Not even a bird was stirring in the green trees beyond the pebbled bar. What big trees! We'd never seen the like. I went down and put a toe cautiously into the water. I could see the bottom all the way across. A quiet little prairie creek from unbroken sod, clear as glass, something not to be found any more. "Let's walk right through!"

We did carefully. When you never saw any flowing water except from a windmill tank, better be careful. Little fish scurried from us. And when we reached the other bank we sat down under the great trees and yelled with delight. Durn the ocean; we'd stay here! Ellis felt something squashy under his pants and yelled, "Plums! I know 'em, just from on the cans Christmas!"

"Pile in an' eat! I'm sure hungry, no breakfast!"

We rolled in red-and-yellow wild plums and ate. They hung from thickets under the trees which were draped in vines with blue wild grapes. We'd never seen any fruit on a tree. It was amazing. We ate and ate and then sighed.

"Ol' Lige won't believe this!" Ellis shouted.

"I'm goin' to take some home fer Effie to cook. I can pack 'em all around inside my shirt to carry home."

Ellis' shirt was all torn around his waist. But he helped fill my shirt. When we waded the great river and started home I was stuffed with plums from neck to pants band. Some felt soft and slippery, but we yelled with triumph of discovery.

I had a time following Ellis. Plums had begun to slip all

around me, down my legs and under my arms. I felt pretty sticky when I joined him. It was after sunset, and a little wind rising. Ellis was studying the prairie northwest, and then I saw what he was watching—a fire line, faint and far in the September grass.

We'd seen fire lines before, mad fast-racing fires reaching to plowed lands and swiftly around them, leaving a black sparking world into which we boys plunged as soon as it cooled enough for bare feet. Spring fires were best because then we saw the white eggs of prairie chickens against the black grass nests and some of them were fit to eat.

We plodded northward in starlight, and soon the wind was rising. We could smell smoke, and when we climbed out of the gully we saw points of leaping fire not half a mile away.

Ellis said, "Say, that's between us an' home. An' one fork is spreadin' south. We better git back to that river an' wait where it goes."

It was all right for Ellis; he could run if he had to. I felt loaded down and sticky with squashed plums. But we knew better than stay in the run of a prairie fire. So we started slowly back, and the smoke grew stronger. Once so thick that we couldn't see the fire line. It was drawing its own wind along, and when we got through the smoke we saw it racing for the timber.

Ellis yelled, "Better git fer that river, Chick! Hurry up!"

That was a fine way to talk. I hurried after him, and plums joggled all around my ribs. Before we got halfway to the timber I fell over some bunch grass and rolled down the draw. I saw Ellis 'way ahead by the fire glow, and he was yelling like he was scared. I got up and ran after him, and we ducked under the first trees, fell over the sandbank and crawled to the plum thickets.

We were too tired to talk. The whole north was alight with racing fires. When it reached the creek bank sparks were whirling through the trees and ash was showering down. We crossed the mighty river knee-deep and crawled into the sand under the plum thickets. I slapped damp sand on my head, for it was pretty hot when the fire was roaring on up the gully in the high grass.

Ellis croaked, "Don't worry—it'll race on east. Won't cross the water with the wind west now." We stretched out in damp sand and soft plums.

When the fires had driven on eastward, leaving a dancing, sparking world around us, I said, "Yeh, we're all right. But we ain't goin' to cross that prairie, hot as it is, barefooted. Got to camp here till daylight."

"How you feel, Chick? Runnin' packed with plums inside yore shirt, you did pretty good."

"I guess. But I'm lathered with plum juice head to foot."

"That won't hurt you, mebbe good fer sores. And I guess we got to eat plums fer supper an' breakfast too."

"I had plenty today. I'm all soft like pie now."

"Won't hurt you. Bed down, dig sand over you an' sleep."

"Yeh. But I'm dang slippery with plum juice."

"Won't kill you. Git to sleep. We roll out early."

Cool September dark came after the winking fires died down. Ellis was asleep in no time. But I got dang chilly. Even sand raked over me was full of plum juice. Leaves and sand stuck to me all over, and black ash from the fires.

When daylight came over the misty flowing water and I got up Ellis raised a whoop. "You don't look like a human bein'!" Then Ellis had one of his bright thoughts which always allowed him to dodge trouble. He yelled, "Say, Effie's goin' to be sore on you sure!"

"Ain't my fault I look like this—ashes, sand an' plum juice. I was tryin' to get some plums home to Effie."

"That's my idea. She'd have a conniption tryin' to get all that stuff out yore shirt an' breeches. We got to gather a lot more an' take home to her. Then she won't jaw us."

I was eating plums for breakfast, but I saw what he meant. He went on arguing. "She says she hasn't seen fresh fruit since Back East startin' fer Californy. Nobody here's got fruit. Come on, we'll git some more!"

"You mean me lug 'em? I ain't no pack horse."

"Won't hurt you. Yore all stuck an' plastered with plum juice now. Another load won't hurt you."

I waddled around, trying to keep my legs from sticking together. Ellis didn't wait. He began shoveling up plums and sand and piling them down inside my neckband. All the time telling how plums would please Effie so she wouldn't be in a state o' mind. Then Ellis led the way up the creek bank to the blackened prairie. Took us a time to locate where home ought to be, for you couldn't see any South Road now. But we started north by the sun. In no time that sun was hot. In an hour I began to feel mean. Dust and ashes we kicked up settled all over me in the plum juice. After another hour with Ellis eating plums out of my shirt for breakfast we saw a house 'way off westward. In another hour we saw Gebauer's white buildings in the sun. But we made a wide travel around them, and in another hour we saw Lige's windmill. We crossed the plowed South Eighty where the fire had stopped here. I was too gummed up to travel fast. Ellis was at the corral, yelling, away head of me.

Lige was in for noon sitting on a wagon tongue. He just stared at me like I was a heathen cannibal.

"Plums!" I yelled. "Fer Effie!" I hoped she was listening. "Looky! All fer Effie to can! Puddin' too!"

"How you git all black an' shiny?"

Ellis said, "Aw, he just fell down a couple o' times in ashes, an' everything stuck to him in plum juice."

"She always said she hadn't seen any fruit since Back East." I started for the soddy, yelling confidently.

Effie came out. "Well, of all things—plums! Where you git 'em?"

"We found a big river full o' plums. Wasn't any ocean down South Road, but I guess we didn't go far enough."

"Peel off yore shirt an' scrape it in a wash boiler. Ellis, you help scrape them plums off his hide. Plums! Never heard o' the like in this prairie country!"

Well, we felt pretty good at what she said. We were always mighty conceited boys, knowing more than grownups. So Ellis and Lige scraped me off in the big wooden washtub. I had to get into the horse trough and wash, and here I'd planned just one bath for Thanksgiving! We talked mighty important now. Lige just listened. He wasn't a hand to go venturing anywhere. Effie grabbed a lot of the best plums and washed them and went to cookin' and singin'. She cooked all afternoon after putting out some corn bread and side meat for us. We hadn't had a thing to eat since day before yesterday except plums.

But when supper came we pitched in again. Big plum puddin' all cooked up with eggs and flour and sody and bacon fat. Lige was so upset he didn't go back to work, and at supper he just sat and shoveled in plum puddin'. Nobody mentioned cyclones or skunks, which had started us off exploring South Road. Couldn't smell skunk on us now.

Lige just said, "I told you boys not to go off traipsin' the prairie, September dry an' fires startin'. Good thing you found that crick to duck into. I heard there was one off south." He shoved down a lot more puddin'.

Effie said, "Oh, let them boys ramble! Findin' fruit like this."

"Next time," I said, "we'll travel West Road. Liable to find Indians Out West."

Effie cried, "My lands, I wish I could go!"

Well, Ellis and I didn't invite her. A woman would be good to cook and wash up camp but not fighting Indians. Effie'd make too much noise, and besides she was too busy at the ranch daylong. So we didn't invite her, just changed the subject.

Then she said, "Where's Earl? He didn't show up fer breakfast either."

"Lost his appetite on account that girl at Gebauer's," said Lige. "How you know a girl was comin' from Germany?"

"Oh, I can keep secrets! Mr. Gebauer told me long time ago. He said she was a pretty girl too. So I began to plan an' figger. I told Earl to light out down there ahead o' everybody to see her."

"Yeh, but Marion Marlow got ahead o' him. Like I

told you, he met her in town an' rode home behind Mr. Gebauer's buggy. You just oughta see a buggy!"

"Oh, Back East I seen plenty o' buggies! You boys don't know much, Chick, never able to get outa Second Reader." Then Effie screwed up her small brown face until her blue eyes twinkled. "So Marion saw her first?"

"Yeh, an' braggin' an' blowin' like he always did. He sure had that girl's eyes bulgin' out, ridin' round the buggy an' whoopin'."

"Now Earl's got to git some store clothes."

"Now, woman, you lay off them two boys. You been readin' that dang book where two knights or somebody git to fightin' about a girl." Lige shoveled in more puddin'.

Effie was excited. "That's right—just like in my book! You know, it's what they call romance, that book."

"Well, them pore waddies ain't goin' to fight fer nothin'. They's good friends, an' you let 'em alone."

"Dry up," said Ellis. "Here comes Earl now fer puddin'." We yelled him in to supper and told him about the big river. But he'd crossed many, trailin' steers in the old days. Effie got him a dishful of puddin'. She said, "Where you been all day an' night? Didn't you know we got a girl in the neighborhood?"

Earl looked kind of ganted up. "Yeh. An' I saw Marion too, down near Gebauer's. We hadn't seen each other fer a whole season, so we bedded down out on the prairie an' talked most o' the night. Had a good talk, I swear. But I never saw a hand duded up like Marion was, that's a fact."

"Don't you let him git ahead o' you, Earl! You git some new clothes too. Don't let any man cut you out!"

Lige said, "Now, look here, woman, what you startin' around here?"

I yelled, "They got to fight like in her book!"

Big lummox Earl just looked so startled he stopped on his puddin'. "Don't need no store clothes. An' I ain't sparkin' ner fightin' about any girl. Well, folks, I got to slope along an' hunt yore Susie-cow who's all the time strayin'." He got his long legs untangled from the table and went out.

I said, "Now Effie made him feel bad again. First about farmin' an' now a dang girl. But I bet he'll never say he can't live without her."

"Like the book," said Ellis. "Books make trouble."

"I want Earl to git her," said Effie. "He's a steady man, not a hellin', shootin' rider like Marion wants to be."

"Oh, Marion ain't clear growed up yet," said Lige. "Now, Effie, don't you go gettin' this neighborhood upset, talkin' about fightin' an' all."

Effie didn't answer us. She went to rattling dishes and singing to herself, looking out to the sky now and then, just happy with something new to think about. Lige went out and sat by the door and listened. If a book made Effie happy singing, he'd put up with it. When I came out he started to pick on me as he liked to do. "Heh-heh! Chick, he found a big river, an' then he bedded down all night in a lot o' plums! Too bad he didn't get caught in that prairie fire, stuffed like he was. Then he'd been baked puddin' an' we'd had him fer supper—heh—heh—bedded down in plums!"

I said, "Well, it's better 'n beddin' down with a skunk in a cyclone hole—heh—heh!"

Effie went to laughing. Lige didn't know what to say. He ambled off and sat by the corral, trying to think of something that would flat down the ears of a smarty like me. When Ellis and I turned in under the old covered wagon he was still pondering how to get even with me. Effie turned down the lamp and went to bed. Took me some time to get to sleep in the hay under the old horse blanket. Didn't see how any girl that didn't know enough to read Second Reader even, like I could, could make trouble for two cowhands what were good friends. But Effie's hard to head off when she wants something. I began to wonder how I could take a hand in it to stop them fellers from fighting. Earl hadn't even seen Miss Frawleen Worsenever yet, so how he say he couldn't live without her? But maybe I'd better do something to start them fellers to fighting. That certainly would please Effie, to make it like in her storybook. She used to nag Earl when he came up from Texas or Indian country to stay with us winters with no wages until he tied into some cow outfit in the spring. But now Effie got sweeted up to Earl, saying how fine it was to homestead land and settle down and grow up with the country. This pore cowpoke didn't know what was in her mind, but I did. She was aiming to get him married, saying how fine it was to farm around here.

# 5

## Miss Frawleen Takes Riding Lessons

Sure enough, when school opened, up drove Miss Frawleen whatever her name was—we called her Miss Worsenever. The pore dummy didn't know what it meant anyhow. The teacher—who boarded at Mr. Gebauer's, for nobody who lived in the sod houses had room for her— was a new one as usual. They were always young girls sent down to No. 4 School to break 'em in the business, I guess; and none of them came back next term. Big snows and all the fights and trouble the big boys made was too much for 'em. But big boys, like the Webels who lived somewhere down south of Gebauer's, didn't start school until fall work was done.

When Teacher rang her bell there were eight girls and five boys besides Ellis and me, and Teacher made a little talk as usual, trying to find out how much anybody knew. I didn't listen. I couldn't find a garter snake to bring to school, so I had a little frog. When I saw how big Miss Worsenever was I took the desk behind her. She looked around and smiled and then listened to Teacher but couldn't understand a bit, I guess.

She was cleaner than any of us, looking pretty good in front, pink with blue eyes and yellow hair. But, sitting right behind her, all I saw was yellow hair and two big red ears all swelled up and peeled on top, for prairie sun wasn't like German, I reckon.

Not having to listen to Teacher, I put my frog up against Miss Frawleen's ear. It wiggled, and then she wiggled. Second time she looked around and the frog got away and jumped. Teacher came down and said, "Take that thing outdoors. What's your name?"

"Chick. Named Thomas, but I never hear it. My father was named Tuttle, an' he was a big Colonel an' run all the Rebels——"

The scholars all began to yell, for I'd said that last year, first day, and had two fights by stating that a colonel was bigger than a general. One of the boys bloodied my nose.

Well, Teacher went back to her desk, and I took the frog out. First day was as usual, pawing around over old books. Teacher spent more time over that big German girl than anybody else, trying to drive some sense into her head. When she asked me I rattled off the Second Reader stuff fine. Teacher seemed surprised. "I thought you were starting Second Reader."

"Heck, no! Been whackin' at it two years."

"Why don't you have a Third Reader?"

"Dang if I know. I guess it's on account the Mortgage, an' Lige too triflin' when he gits to town, Effie says."

"I must go talk with your family about you."

"No, you don't! Stay away from our place. We got the dangest worse dogs you ever see! Don't come snoopin' around."

Miss Frawleen looked around at the row. Teacher knew a little Dutch, and they both jabbered about me and pointed.

Well, first day let out, and everybody started home across the prairie. Ellis was heading north to the Buffalo Waller, where we always went after any trouble. I didn't get out, Teacher wanting to talk to me. The big girl from the Old Country waited outside in Mr. Gebauer's buggy.

Before Teacher could start nagging me I spoke up first. "Look here, what fer that long-legged lummix start to our school? She don't know enough—can't even read Second Reader like me."

"She wants to learn English. She went to school in Germany, of course. Away ahead of Second Readers——"

"Yeh? You aim to say she knows more 'n I do?"

"Certainly. She's here just to get English."

"Well, I figger that anybody can't talk 'Merican talk is plumb ignorant. How she goin' to read any books either?"

"She's read more books than any of us——"

"What you mean? German folks got books? Foreign folks got books? French boys got books? Chinee boys got books?"

Teacher began laughing. People always did when I got to telling them anything. I got out and headed for the Waller before she could ask me any more stuff. Well, that was news to me—foreign folks, too dumb to talk English, having books! Across the prairie, in Mr. Gebauer's buggy, I heard that longlegs and Teacher laughing in Dutch, and it made me sore again. They wouldn't see me in school tomorrow. So I got to work in Effie's vegetable patch. Effie tried to raise flowers too, but that German, Gebauer, had more flowers than anybody. But all around our place were the little wild roses that grew in prairie grass, and nobody had to care for them. Heathen like us, Effie said.

Fall chores were busy times for boys big enough to work. Effie jawed some about Ellis and me quitting school after first day as usual, but she went to singing around the soddy and forgot it. Things were pretty peaceful until one Saturday when Mr. Gebauer drove Miss Worsenever up to our ranch, talked with Effie and then went on to town. Ellis and I stayed out behind the corral. After a while Effie called to us. She said, "Mr. Gebauer wants Miss Frawleen to learn to ride a horse. She's never been on one. Gebauer's animals aren't saddle-broke, and he wants a safe one like Tops. So you and Ellis teach her to ride."

"Now, looka here, Effie, one o' them cowpokes can learn her to ride. Where's Earl now? Or Marion, him all shined up for women anyhow?"

"Marion's down at his kinfolks' 'way South. Earl, he's off lazin' around the north section, watchin' Lige husk corn. So you git out my ol' sidesaddle and put it on Tops."

Ellis and me put up a holler, but didn't do any good. I wanted to get Lige's saddle, but Effie wouldn't have it. "You know well enough it ain't proper fer a woman to ride straddle."

"Yeh? Why ain't it?"

"It ain't polite to look at a woman's legs, an' you know it. So git my ol' sidesaddle an' clean it."

It sure needed cleaning. Effie had never used it since she came out here, but the chickens had. It hung on a nail in the horse shed where chickens roosted everywhere they could hang on. Ellis and I oiled and loosened and scraped an hour on that old stiff sidesaddle, and we were pretty mad about it.

Then we got it over Ol' Tops's bony back and cinched.

That ol' bugger was goin' to be surprised when he found a woman on his back too ignorant to talk English. Tops was a tall, shaggy old horse safe enough for anybody, for he hated to get out of a walk. I wasn't tall enough myself to get on Tops's back except by climbing on the windmill tank.

Ellis said, "Better git her on the frame an' hist. If she never been on a horse, I'll lead Tops around an' you steady Miss Frawleen in that dang sidesaddle."

"Yeh? I can't even reach her except to grab her foot, an' Effie says it ain't proper to see women's legs."

Well, we hollered for them to come out. Effie started to jaw us how to be careful and all, and Miss Worsenever all smiling under a pink parasol on account of her peeled ears.

I pointed for her to climb on the tank frame and then she could pull over into the sidesaddle and Ellis could lead the outfit around the yard and the dummy would learn something maybe. Well, Miss Worsenever slid over all right, but she went too far, and I grabbed her foot and shoved up to steady her. Shut my eyes; didn't even look at her foot, as was proper. Then I heard a yell from Ellis and a shriek from Miss Frawleen and a big splash in the windmill tank.

Effie dashed over to me and said, "Now see what you done! Miss Frawleen in the tank."

"The bellyband busted, that's what. Or we got too

much oil on that ol' saddle. Hell, that won't hurt her in the tank a minute."

Ellis yelled to me, "Light out o' here! Earl's comin' on a lope!"

I lit out across the West Eighty for the Buffalo Waller. The Waller was the place where it seemed like home after you were in a fix. I jumped over the rim down into the sand and crawled into the dugout, my back against the dirt wall where we'd cut out a shelf for a bed place. Cool and dim back in there. There I waited until Ellis came.

He said, "You better not go home till folks gone to bed. They'll skin you alive. Earl had a time fishin' Miss Frawleen outa the tank. Effie had to lend her some dry clothes an' put hers out to dry. Earl said you did it apurpose."

"It was me tryin' to be polite. When I shoved her foot up, which is proper with my eyes shut, over she goes off Ol' Tops. If she'd rode straddle, she'd stuck on."

"She cussed you in Dutch. Well, anyhow she got to meet Earl, which Effie wanted to happen."

I was digging in the old feedbox we'd hooked from the ranch. There was always some moldy bread and dried meat, some kind of stuff to eat, and we didn't care much what it was. We went to the ranch away after dark in starlight and crawled under the wagon on the hay. Wet or dry, somebody got Miss Frawleen home to Gebauer's.

The next morning Lige said to me, "What's this I hear, you dumpin' this girl from the Old Country into our windmill tank?"

"Can't blame me or Ol' Tops. We was actin' proper."

"Earl fished her out. But it's a doggone pore way fer a man to meet a girl, wet like that."

I thought Effie'd be madder than tunket at me, but she wasn't much. Pretty soon she laughed and got breakfast.

"My lands, it's just like the book! The damsel gits into trouble, an' the hero gallops up an' rescues her from the villain! Now I see it all workin' out fine."

Lige said, "There you go, woman, about that fool story-book."

"Marion Marlow can be the villain. He kidnaps the girl an' hides her in the cave!"

"What the hell fer?" I said.

Effie was so dreamy she didn't even hear I was cussing. Made me feel pretty good, like I was a grown man.

Ellis said, "Well, there ain't no caves around here except the Buffalo Waller, mebbe like a cave."

"That's it! That's the place!"

Ellis and I put up another roar. "No, you don't! We ain't ever goin' to have any woman in the Buffalo Waller! Any villain around here's got to lug her somewheres else."

"Oh, you don't understand! Git out the house an' let me think! In the book the hero is an earl like our Earl. You all scoot out o' here."

Back of the corral, hitching up, Lige said, "Well, I swan! Chick, she thinks now you fixed it all up right so's Earl could come ridin' up an' rescue a girl. He got splashed wet too."

"Mebbe he saw her legs, which ain't proper. Well, I ain't goin' back to school until this excitement settles down, everybody hearin' I shoved a woman off a horse into a water tank."

"Yeh," said Lige. "I sure want peace around yere."

So I didn't hear much more about it, but I stayed away

from Miss Worsenever. At school I wouldn't even look at her, and she wouldn't speak to me. Suited me fine.

Marion Marlow came up from where he stayed with some kinfolk over south beyond Plum Creek or somewhere and stayed to supper with us. Had on all his buckaroo clothes too, which he wouldn't dare wear into town at Jake's Saloon or any place cowhands could see him. The soddy was pretty hot when we got around the table. Marion took off his Mexican jacket with all the big brass buttons and braid and hung it outside on a post. His big hat too, with the jingle bells on it. When four grownups ate at the table Ellis and me had to wait outside, but there'd be plenty left, eating second.

"Effie seems dang pleased to have Marion come in. If he's the villain, he don't even know it," Ellis said.

I was fingering over Marion's fancy jacket, and then I smelled the beads and braid. Then I smelled close. Then I motioned Effie outside when she was at the stove for another plate of fried chicken. "Look, Marion's outfit smells just like yore Californy dress packed in the trunk. His hat does too."

She smelled them. "Camphor balls, that's a fact. Now, that is funny. But don't you boys say a thing right now about it."

Well, we didn't. But it was funny. Cowhands smelled like cows, and horses; dogs maybe, and leather, and cigars and whisky and perfume if they come from town, but none ever smelled like he'd been packed in a trunk. Effie went back dubious, warning us.

But I went to thinking. Another plumb mystery to settle. Earl and Marion came out to cool off, picking their teeth, not knowing Effie was planning to get them into a fight over Miss Frawleen. Pretty soon she'd call on me to help again.

Things got quiet at the ranch. Marion Marlow, after eating with us for a week—and welcome, like everybody that camped near Lige—went off south to his kinfolks to stay. Sometimes he wore his buckaroo clothes, but he didn't dare wear them to town with Earl. He had more money than I ever saw a herd rider show, and he'd bring back a bottle of whisky for Lige. Lige would hide it out in the straw barn, but Effie knew all about it. Earl Staley would take a snifter with them, but he wasn't a hard-drinking hand. Marion would fetch Effie something from town. Once he brought her a little chiny dog that held pepper. He said that now the store was going to have ice cream, something we'd never seen. Effie said maybe the country was civilized with ice cream. Marion fetched Ellis a jackknife, but I wouldn't have one, for my old toad stabber made out of a busted bayonet was better than any store knife.

With Marion gone we didn't hear so much of cow business and how jobs was scarce unless a man wanted to ride winters, and what for if you could hole up till spring? Then I heard Earl talking about land in Custer County where a man could homestead.

"Now," Effie said to me, "what you think? I got him started to settle down. I'm goin' to get him married to Miss Frawleen!"

"That pore cowhand'll just bust up with a Mortgage like Lige got. An' he's too scared of women except you."

"Chick, you help me egg him on to marryin' Frawleen."

Well, I got hold of Earl once when finally he gave in to Effie and said he'd go look at land in Custer County. But I didn't mention Miss Frawleen by name. I just said he'd better light out of this country so he wouldn't get in a fuss with Marion Marlow.

He was startled, then he hollered, mad at me, "Yore dam' tootin' right I ain't fussin' with anybody, let alone my best friend—Marion. You keep outa my business."

"It ain't me, it's Effie. She says yore just like a big brother to that feller but you got to have a fight. An', say, how come Marion come up from Texas with so much spendin' money?"

Earl gave me a funny look and shook his head. Well, that was enough for me. Ellis had come along, and his eyes stuck out when I yelled, "Can't fool me! Marion's robbed a bank or somethin'!"

"Gee!" said Ellis. "That's so? Why, he's a bigger man than Jesse James now, ain't he?"

Earl gave me the meanest look I ever saw. "Here, don't go sayin' things like that about a friend o' mine."

Effie had come out of the soddy, hearing this row. Now she was excited. "Robbed a train, mebbe! That's what I want—a villain. Mystery! Ain't it, Earl?"

Earl, he backed off. He said, "Well, mebbe it is mystery. Marion does act kinda funny since he came back from ridin' roundups this time. For a fact, he does."

"An' smells like camphor balls fer bugs," I yelled. "How about that now?"

Earl backed farther away. "You all let that boy alone."

Ellis said, "Effie wants you an' him to git in a fight over that girl from the Old Country. But first you got to buy a suit o' store clothes to shine up better 'n a buckaroo."

Earl backed farther and slid a leg over his pony. "I got to git to town. But I don't need no store clothes. I ain't sparkin' or fightin' anybody. Honest, Effie, just lemme alone."

# 6

# The Great Indian War (West Road)

Ellis AND I determined to explore Out West before
the weather got so cold that all the Indians would hole up
for winter and we wouldn't find any. Out West, on the
Joggerfee map, was a line of little jagged marks that stood
for mountains, and an Indian chief with a feather headdress and a tomahawk. On the upper side of our map was
an Eskimo dressed in furs, standing by a snow hut with
some dogs.

Ellis said, "That's North. I ain't goin' to start that way
with winter comin'. The Eskimo feller looks half froze."

"Me either. Lige says all they got to eat is whales. He
says French folks eat frogs, Eskimos eat whales, Indians
eat dogs an' them plug-hat New York folks eat all kinds
o' fancy stuff like wine that pore fellers Out West with a
Mortgage can't think of."

The farthest North we'd been yet was the Rooshins'
place. Nobody knew much about them; they didn't send
their baby-kids down to our school. They were taught by
a funny little priest with a round black cap and whiskers.
The three men of the colony all had big black whiskers
too, and they laughed a lot but didn't know much English. Just ignorant foreign folks, I thought. But they had
the biggest house around there, plastered white inside and

out. I was there once to dinner when their boss man, Toby somebody, hired me to ride lead horse on his three-team harvester when they cut wheat. They didn't have a boy big enough to ride the wheat line. I had the best dinner you'd ever see, ate with the men, and their women waited on us, then dodged out of sight with the baby-kids.

Three families lived in the long house. You went through a door from the kitchen and were right in the horse barn! Next the cow stalls, then the pigs at the end. All under one roof, warm and fine. A boy wouldn't have to wade snow to do chores as we did at Lige's. I rode lead horse for two days, and at home folks wanted to know what kind of folks Rooshins were.

Well, they treated me fine. And everybody thought they wouldn't. Toby gave me half a dollar a day to help harvest. But all day, dawn to dark, I rode that harnessed critter with just a sack stuffed with hay, and second day when I started home Big Toby yelled at me and pointed at my legs. I was chafed until now the blood was seeping through my pants.

Toby hollered and got me in a rig and took me home. He seemed all upset, but I couldn't understand his talk. Lige said he wanted to know why I didn't complain, all cut up by harness buckles like that. "Them Rooshins feel terrible, you not tellin' 'em."

"Well, I wasn't goin' to holler. Indians don't yell—you can stick pins or arrows in an Indian an' he just sneers at you."

"Damn Indians! Here's the dollar Toby says you earned, but you can't work no more off this place. Effie'll have to dose you up with somethin'."

"I don't want any dosin' on my legs. I'd like a swig o' Pain Killer outa Effie's trunk if she'd give it to me."

"No, she won't. On the bottle it says 'Good fer Consumption,' but it tastes like whisky an' that's why you want it. You stay from school till you get well."

"Sure I will. But them Rooshins are fine folks even if they don't want to mix with anybody else. They got a little priest there with a little black cap who's boss o' the whole outfit. And why don't we have a big fine house an' good fences an' machinery like foreigners got?"

Lige looked off west kind of pained. "Well, we will someday, unless we pull up stakes an' start fer Californy like I meant to when I left Back East. Ain't no use fixin' things here. Whole outfit! Chick, we'll load the wagon an' start!"

Lige had been saying that for years, and Effie'd laugh. "Just a shiftless mountain man," she'd say. "Just big talk an' no go. Lige is set here fer life."

Maybe Lige was, but Ellis and me weren't. We figured on West Road before winter set in. We wanted to take the muskit along, but Ellis had got the ramrod fast in it again in a newspaper wad and we'd have to burn it out somehow. The threshing crew came along, and we stayed from school to help out. It was exciting when the threshers came. They had ten horses on the power machine, and round and round they went all day long. Effie got Miss Frawleen Worsenever up to help her cooking—boiled beef, chicken and garden stuff—and you could hardly get around in the soddy for pies and cakes piled everywhere. Threshing men were the biggest eaters you ever saw. The boss man ran the horsepower. Two fellers forked the

bundles from the stacks to Ellis, who was bandcutter. Lige
sacked the wheat that came rolling out the spout. Boys
always got the worst jobs, like me stacking straw. The
chaff and straw rolled down all over me. In no time I was
chin-deep in it. Earl Staley had his pony out of the corral
early to go look after the stock westward, for this farmwork just wasn't his line. But when he saw me buried in
straw he scratched his ear, got a pitchfork and pitched in
to help. He'd been pretty grumpy with me ever since I
upset Frawleen in the tank.

"Hey, you Chick, get back from under the straw carrier
afore they have to dig you out! Let me take this side."

Well, that was something to see. A cowhand at farming! In no time Earl was covered with dust and chaff too.
All morning we shoved straw, and the thresher roared, and
the boss larruped the horses. Lige got his little rickety
granary full and then went to piling wheat on the ground
as usual. He aimed to take that to town, but, as usual, rain
and snow would come first and he couldn't market the
stuff.

Earl and I didn't talk much until noon when we washed
up after the crew had gone in to eat. Earl had to be second-
table with Lige and us boys, but he spent so much time
trying to get wheat beards out of his shirt he was late
even there.

Ellis yelled, "Look at ol' Earl startin' farmwork!"

Effie said, "Don't pester Earl. He's goin' to Custer
County an' homestead land. Goin' to stay an' grow up
with folks!"

I knew what she meant. She was aiming for that feller

to get married an' settle down. I said, "He ain't got a pot
or pan to start housekeepin' on."

Earl gave me another hard look and wouldn't say anything. After dinner the crew rested around, trying to find
shade along the sod wall. Earl was out by the corral, trying to fish the scratchy wheat beards out of his shirt. I
didn't try, for I knew we'd have it worst in afternoon. The
stuff got you sore all over before night.

At dark we were washing up at the horse trough. Then
the crew ate up the rest of Effie's fixin's and started to
knock down their gear. The big day was over. There was
the bright straw piled all over the cow-barn poles and the
wheat piled higher than your head.

I said to Earl, "Now's your chance. Somebody's got to
take Miss Frawleen down to Gebauer's. You got to take
the grain wagon."

Earl grunted. "Chick, you keep outa my business, will
you?"

"What you sore about? If it hadn't been fer me, you'd
never had a chance to rescue Miss Frawleen out the tank—
so romantic, as Effie says."

"You let me alone!" Earl said and went to hitch up.

Miss Frawleen was in the soddy, rattling dishes with
Effie. Lige was figuring how many bushels of wheat he'd
got. The thresher crew had pulled out in the dark. The
boss wouldn't get paid till Lige hauled wheat. Effie came
out and called to Earl. I knew she was going to get him
to take ol' Worsenever home even if they couldn't talk
much. When Earl came back I said, "Look, don't let her
fall out that wagon. She don't know much in this country.

If a woman gets upside down, her feet stickin' out, you shut yore eyes an' say 'Much obliged,' polite like Effie wants."

"You scramble out o' here afore I cuff you!"

"I'm just tellin' you what Effie says. I guess it's in the Bible."

"You lay off me. I read the Bible back in Arkansaw when I wasn't bigger 'n you. I wasn't brung up a heathen like you."

Well, Frawleen climbed in over the wheel and talked German to Earl, and off they rattled in the dark. Effie said, "There! I knew I could fix it. I told Gebauer not to come in his buggy so Earl'd have to take her home."

Lige said, "Woman, you'll play hell yet, perusin' around in other folks' business. How's Earl goin' to talk to her?"

"Don't need to talk, German or English or anything, when yore in love."

"Oh, my cracky, *love!*" I yelled. "Just somethin' outa that book!"

Effie went back and started on the dishes. She made me and Ellis dry them. And she sung to herself, a little skinny woman like that, and been up before daylight, working the big dinner for the threshers. Lige dodged any help cleaning up and went to bed. Ellis and I went out and bedded under the covered wagon. My skin was so itchy with wheat beards I couldn't sleep much.

But Ellis said, "Looks like might snow early this fall. We better start out tomorry an' travel West Road. We can ride Tops an' Jewel, fer they didn't work today. You get in the house after Effie goes to bed an' sneak some bread an' salt pork out here fer tomorry."

I was pretty stiff and bunged up, but I said, "Yeh. Mebbe we can get far enough to find Indians, but I guess not."

I got the food, and afterwhile I did go to sleep. I felt pretty sore after threshing, but Indians don't holler when they're hurt, so I wasn't going to holler. You can stick pins in 'em, an' . . . an' . . . they sneer . . . but how does a man sneer? I tried to, but it made me sneeze—and put me to sleep.

When I woke up on account of scratching my ribs I thought of Earl Staley. He'd have to scratch himself too, and he couldn't say that he couldn't live without her, itching like that. He couldn't even say what ailed him in German. I bet this first lick of farmwork he ever did would settle him. If he had any sense, he'd pack and slope out for cow country, get a job and keep away from women. But maybe he didn't have enough sense. Most grownups didn't seem to have much sense, it seemed to me.

Well, Ellis jabbed me awake, and I crawled out in dawn coming and it was pretty cool. If I walked around, I itched, head to foot. I didn't think much of farming either right then, the jobs a boy got on a farm. Ellis had Tops and Jewel out of the corral and led Tops by the tank so I could get on. I didn't have a saddle since that outlaw cayuse started for Texas with my old wreck on him. But I rolled up some wheat sacks under a ragged blanket and slid onto Tops's back. Tops didn't want to travel either. Ellis got 'way ahead of us and was past the schoolhouse when daylight came. I ambled along and caught up a mile farther on, and that was far as we'd ever been Out West. The road was just a few wagon marks in the dried grass.

Not many emigrant outfits came along this way any more, for now they could travel by train 'way up north of us. This country was just big and peaceful, and, as the grasshopper years were past, folks didn't leave any more for Back East. Some stuck like Lige and Effie, but that was before I was big enough to remember bad grasshopper years. Effie warned they'd come again and eat us out of house and home this time. There'd be nothing left but the dang Mortgage and maybe Ol' Tops, who was one of the team they'd started with from Wisconsin to Californy. Tops was a regular old critter, stiff all the time like me now full of wheat stickers. But now he was headed west again— toward Californy! By sunup I felt more spry.

Ol' Tops didn't. Ellis was half a mile ahead of me Out West on Jewel, but then Jewel was younger. She hadn't started for Californy when she was young, like Tops, and landed here in the middle of America. Tops was tough. He never stopped going, but I couldn't kick him off a walk.

We didn't see many houses, and we kept well away from them. When we tried to get back on West Road it wasn't much except a few ruts where wagon folks had passed. Open-range country with white bones scattered some places where stock had died. It wasn't any place to winter cattle, grass under big snows and no water. Last cow outfit had quit, and settlers kept their stock under fence now.

Ellis and I ate some bread and meat in a little gully out of the wind and then went on. It was near sundown when I rode up to him. He said, "I guess we got to camp all night. There's a little water down in this draw fer the horses an' good grass around it. Start home tomorry."

"Hell, no! Ain't seen a thing yet but prairie. I don't figger we'll git to any mountains, but every mile we git closer."

We struck a match in some bunch grass and had a little fire. It got colder after dark. I had the old horse blanket I rode on Tops. We pulled it over us in the draw out of the wind. In an hour I began to wish we were home under the covered wagon with all the dogs piled around us as they always did. Well, a feller will sleep finally if he's tired enough, and we sure were.

The sun was about up when Ellis gave me a shove. He said, "Listen. I hear somebody talkin'!"

I crawled up, feeling pretty stiff. Frost was sparkling all around on the grass. Ellis was listening at the top of the draw. "I sure hear somebody!"

"Coyotes. Ain't nobody out here."

Ellis crawled higher in the grass. Then he crawled back, and he was so pale his freckles looked faded, kinda blue. He got up close to me and whispered, "Indians!"

"Yeah?"

"Keep yore head down but go look down the draw."

I crawled higher. Sure enough, two boys were looking down at our horses near the water hole. And beyond them I saw three big Indians staring our way. And across on the other side I saw some ponies, hitched to a pole drag, and couple of women beside a fire. Indians, all right, but I never heard a whoop out of 'em.

Ellis said, "They got us surrounded. We're in a fix. Wish we'd brought the muskit. I got my little knife an' you got the big toad stabber."

"They ain't no good fightin'. Mebbe we can sneak away."

"They got our horses. If we run outa this gully, they can shoot us right out in the open, not even a tumbleweed to hide in. So you think o' what to do, you always so smart. I thought yesterday we was goin' too far west. Chick, think o' somethin'!"

I couldn't think of a thing. But I crawled closer to get a better look at the three warriors. They looked funny for Indians. Not like in the Joggerfee book. No feathers, no spears and arrows, no war paint. Just brown men with black hair, and dressed in any kind of old clothes like we did.

One had a carbine under his arm, but I didn't see a tomahawk nor war club.

In a way I felt disappointed. I looked at their camp, where a fat woman was chopping brush with a busted ax. They had five horses, and everybody looked ganted and tired as if they'd run a long way from the soldiers. But nobody came near us. They all just stared at us, not a yell from 'em.

I crawled down the draw out of sight. Ellis looked pretty scared. "How we goin' to save the horses even if they don't scalp us?"

"Dang it, we're surrounded. No use fightin'. I'm goin' to give 'em a parley like we want to be friends."

So I went out and stood up right in the open. Only Indian talk I knew were the four Pawnee words I learned at school, but, being so awful, I was afraid to use them. Might start shooting.

So I went closer and yelled, "Hey, there!"

Ellis said, "Don't start any cussin'. Mebbe they know some English. Better kinda laugh an' smile at 'em so they see you ain't serious an' aimin' to make trouble."

"You edge down towards the horses. If we could git on 'em, we could slope outa here. Only I can't git Ol' Tops to lift a leg faster 'n a walk. No, we got to make a peace talk so them redskins'll understand. Lige says they smoke a big pipe when they want to be friends."

I looked again at the war party. "They ain't got any pipes, and us either. I'm goin' close an' holler to them boys. They ain't got any gun like the big Indians have. If anybody starts shootin' at me, you better leg out fer home an' tell Effie what happened."

So I went closer and studied the outfit better. I yelled again and waved my hat, and, as they didn't move, I walked faster toward them.

Ellis grunted. "You be careful. Don't start 'em fightin'."

Now the whole camp had discovered us. The two women, three men and four boys. They all just stood froze stiff, looked like. Not a word. "A lot o' brown-faced mizzable folks travelin' through the country," I said. "They ain't fightin' now. They look kinda scared, or anyhow don't know what to say. Dang it, they ain't like Indians in the Joggerfee book at all." Well, I was too nervous to stand there doing nothing. I wanted the horses if we could get 'em without fighting.

So I yelled again and walked toward the boys by Ol' Tops and Jewel. The nags just kept on chewing grass an' kicking flies, not worried a bit. One of the Indian horses nickered, and Ol' Tops just raised an ear and kept on eating. I walked right up to his head. Now if they were going to attack us, it'd be the time. Right up close, the Indian boys just stared at me—not a grin, not a word.

I said, "Hey! How! These our horses all right."

Boys, black eyes and hair long below ears, brown thin faces and old blue ragged shirts—I guess from the Army, what they'd took off soldiers after scalpin' 'em like Lige said. I rubbed Tops's nose and said "Hey" again an' laughed. They didn't laugh or nothing. The men never moved, nor the women by their cart. I led Tops an' Jewel right past the whole outfit, an' nobody moved. It was the dangest Indian fight you ever saw. Not a whoop even from anybody. Ol' Tops was so tall I had to pull and haul his neck down to get on, not having the windmill frame as I did at home. Ellis come out the grass now and got on Jewel, him having a saddle.

He whispered to me, "Say, what's the matter? Not a peep from 'em. I bet they're scared. I bet they're travelin' north, tryin' to get back to their reservation in Dakoty before the Army finds they lit out south."

So I pointed north. The biggest boy pointed and nodded. The littlest boy wasn't big as I was, and he looked hungry and dirty.

Ellis said, "Why, the pore little shaver got sore eyes too! Ain't we got some corn bread an' sowbelly left in the sack?"

I untied the grain sack from Ellis' saddle. We'd taken a lot of corn bread and side meat along on this trip, for on the Joggerfee map over southwest was a blank space which said: GREAT AMERICAN DESERT. If so, then there wouldn't be much to eat out there—if we got that far. Maybe these Indian folks had come out from the Great American

Desert, which was why the boys looked so hungry and peaked. I upended the grub sack.

Ellis yelled, "Aw, give 'em the whole durn lot! We're headed home, an' if these Indians would trail along after us we'd feed the whole outfit big."

But we just slid the sack to the ground. They didn't say anything, and we didn't either. Anyhow the Indian boys looked into the sack and then up at us. Their black eyes stared, but they didn't say a word. The big Indians were off by their camp, watching us.

Ellis said, "Best time to skedaddle outa here is when they're eatin'." He whacked Jewel, and she started Back East. I kicked Tops after them. A quarter of a mile on I looked back. All the Indians were about the grain sack now, looking in it, then off to us riding away. They didn't give a war whoop nor raise a tomahawk.

"Well," Ellis said, "we found redskins all right, but this was the dangest Indian fight I ever heard of! Come on, Chick."

I poked along behind on Tops. In a way we were disappointed. Not a whoop even to tell Lige about. I said, "I guess they're too hungry an' played-out to fight anybody. Nothin' to eat. Dogs is good fer Indians, but they ain't got a dog."

"Ate 'em all up. If they'd come with us, we'd give 'em a dog."

"Yeh, I'd give 'em that Stealer dog who don't trust me any. A young dog like that mebbe they could fry fer breakfast."

"Come on. Makes me hungry to talk. Take us all day to git home."

We rode on, and it was nightfall, cold and dark, when we saw a lantern out at the corral. Lige cussing because he had to milk, and Effie lighting the lamp on the oilclothed table. It was pretty nice and warm in the sod house, and I kept thinking of that littlest Indian boy who had sore eyes. Kept wondering if he was warm tonight. Lige asked where in hell we'd been again, and when we said a piece Out West and met Indians he said I was just bragging again, for there weren't any Indians nearer now than Rosebud agency Up North with plenty of soldiers to watch 'em. Effie said, "I'm glad you fed 'em what you had. Now they'll feel friendlier to white folks the next they meet."

"I only wish you'd been along with a pan o' fried cakes an' made 'em all laugh like you do folks."

"Oh, I wish I could go sometimes with you boys just traipsin'!" Effie's eyes shone like they did when she read in her book about love. Then she said, "I declare, it's a shame! White folks killed all the game out this country, so Indians have nothin' to eat any more."

"Yeh," I said. "These folks didn't even have a dog left to eat. Wish I'd had Stealer along, an' the Indian boys could have had a good breakfast."

I looked at the door where the lamplight fell out on the packed yard dirt. Stealer had been sitting there, watching me eat, but when he heard what I said he went back a piece and sat on his tail. He was like that Miss Frawleen Worsenever who didn't trust me no more after she got dumped in the windmill tank. And me, I didn't have hard feelings against anybody, just willing to forgive and forget.

Took me a long time to sleep, thinking of that littlest Indian boy with sore eyes and no salve to rub on them.

Ellis and I had always been for fighting Indians, but personally we had a great admiration for them. That was why we wanted to sleep outdoors under the wagon, for Indians didn't sleep in a house and we wanted to live like them as much as we could. I told Ellis that sometime we'd cut up a dog and see how he tasted, but Ellis raised such a row I didn't mention it again.

# 7

# The Hanged Man's Son (North Road)

TEACHER BROUGHT a new book to school one day
and lined up the biggest scholars in front of her desk. Miss
Frawleen was with them, taller than anybody, even
Teacher. Well, this was a new learning I'd never heard of.
So all the rest of us quit studying the Readers and Spellers
to listen. Teacher gave a little talk first. This book was
all about people's insides.

Ellis listened awhile and said, "She says it's Frizzology
an' it's got pictures accordin' to which people are just like
a cow or pig inside. Chick, you believe that?"

"No, I don't. Who'd cut up folks to see what's inside
'em? Nobody except a dang doctor would be mean as
that. I bet I'm not like a cow inside. Guts is all soft an'
squirmy, an' I don't feel that way."

"If we got to study that, I'm goin' to quit school ag'in."

"Yeh. But look at Miss Worsenever. She's excited like
she knew all about this Frizzology. Mebbe she studied it
in the Old Country, an' 'way ahead of us. Some foreign
stuff."

The big boys looked kind of uneasy about that book.
It wound up with Teacher and Miss Frawleen rattling
away in Dutch and English, for Miss Frawleen had got a

lot of our words now. Well, Ellis an' me didn't listen to any more. We knew better.

In November Lige butchered for the winter's meat, and that was always a fine bloody festival for us, carrying buckets of hot water from the soddy to dump in the barrel. Lige scalded the hogs to get the hair loose. We always stayed away from school for big events like butchering. Steers and pigs were either shot or hit in the head with an ax. That was Earl's job, but sometimes he wasn't with us. Ellis and I helped skin and saw bones and hauled on the rope to swing critters to a pole frame. Then we'd lug the guts from a steer away out on the prairie with the dogs hanging on. We made balloons out of bladders and tomahawks out of shoulder bones.

All in all, a fine festival week in the first good cold snap. Another interesting fiesta was when Lige operated on pigs and calves, usually in spring. We held legs while they bawled and squealed, but it didn't seem to hurt them long. Effie didn't want to hear of these doings. She had a funny modesty. A bull was a gentleman cow, she said, and we mustn't mention boars in her presence either. But after a bull calf was operated on he'd grow up to be a fine gentleman and wouldn't hook or chase cows. Lige and Ellis and I would sit by the corral and laugh, wiping bloody hands on the grass.

But Lige didn't know that out on the prairie when we'd dug a gopher out of his hole we'd operate on him too and then turn him loose, expecting that now he'd grow up fat and gentle as the calves did. But we'd never see the critters again. Maybe they died as did the baby chicks we helped out of their shells and tried to make walk. Most died. Sometimes we'd find a cow out on the prairie having a calf. We'd sit patiently by and then haul the calf out when it first showed. A sow would get the same mid-wifing help, but sometimes they were dangerous when we lugged their newborn offspring about. We didn't think we were cruel. A dang doctor would hurt you worse than that if he got hands on you. But we never saw a doctor; and nobody died either.

So seasons passed. But Lige used to wonder why his young pigs grew up sway-backed and calves were bow-legged and had crooked ears. He never knew our clinics. It was all part of our seeking the mystery of life. Many an old rooster was caught and turned upside down to see why he chased hens and then crowed about it. After a while we would give up examining mysteries and would go back to school to please Effie. If Teacher knew any mysteries of life, she didn't tell us, but we never thought that any teacher knew much anyway.

Ellis said, "Mebbe it's in that Frizzology book that Teacher an' Miss Worsenever gabble about. Miss Fraw-leen acts like she knew all about it in the Old Country, what's inside you."

"Effie says she knows more 'n anybody around here, but it's all in Dutch. What in heck will Earl do if he settles down an' marries her like Effie wants? I'm goin' to ask the big lummix."

So when Earl was with us again I got him alone and said, "Say, why don't you an' Frawleen hitch up like Effie wants? She's the only girl around here big enough, an' not knowin' much English won't hurt. Cows don't know English either, but they move when you knock 'em

around. I want to see somebody git married. Why don't
you?"

Earl had blue eyes, and they shone wicked in the lantern light. "Look here, boy, stay outa my business or I'll
cuff you down."

"Well, I'm just tryin' to help. You go grab Miss Frawleen an' make her holler. An' kiss her. I never saw anybody get kissed."

Earl just shoved me clear out in the dark. He certainly
was mad. So I never saw anybody get kissed until I was
nineteen. Then I tried it myself. It wasn't much to brag
about.

Looking back after these older years, I wonder at the
lack of imagination, our total disinterest in abstractions.
Take God, now. He was all right, whatever He was. Just
trust Him to run things. He would anyhow, and no use
asking Him about it. He wasn't anything to worry about.
The same went for the Devil too; he was another far-off
vagueness. I thought of him as a thin, shaky sort of being
always willing to make you trouble, but he was terribly
scared of God and would skitter out of sight if God came
around. Religion was like law and politics and learning,
something entirely out of our knowledge, so we weren't
interested. Our small world was enough. Everything else
was like Lige's ocean—so big you couldn't see it, so why
bother your head? Ellis and I used to greet every sunrise
with yells of appreciation as we did a new kind of bug
discovered in Effie's garden. We were always whooping
about something we hadn't known before. And accepting
it without question. All about us were the lives of crea-
tures, birth and death, blood and pain, cold and heat—the

known order of things and not to be changed in any way we knew of. The first thinking men must have thought much the same until they evolved superstitions and began to frighten themselves with them.

But our world was expanding. Wagon folks said that now there was a new railroad not so far Up North as the first one. Lige and Effie weren't much excited. They'd seen railroads Back East. But Ellis and I hadn't or even imagined them. Lige said if we ever saw one to light out quick. A durn engine would go faster than anything around here.

Well, we better find out when fall work let up. Marion Marlow, the mysterious fancy cowboy, hadn't ridden up from his cousin's lately, and Earl looked mighty serious. So did Effie after Earl pulled out again for his claim—if he had one. Big boys stayed home for fall husking, and Ellis and I had that excuse for not going back to school. September was a mean month, hot; and ranch women were too fagged out with summer to go gadding to see other places. We boys went weeks without seeing another person except Lige and Effie. But we were never lonesome; dawn to dark there seemed much to do and argue about.

Lige plowed the potato field, and Ellis and I dug and piled the potatoes up. Then no one knew what to do with so many. Turnips, beets and root crops would come in after the first touch of frost. They would be piled near the house, and then we'd dig pits for winter storage under dirt and snow, as usual, but most of the yields would rot. Lige had no time to try to market them, and nobody cared anyway. I wondered why we raised stuff to spoil. But a dirt farmer didn't know what to do except raise food crops. Lige said the Railroad was to blame for all this.

Next to the New Yorkers and their Mortgage, the Railroad was the great enemy. Lige borrowed a weekly paper once in a while and slowly wormed his way through it. Then vast was his wrath at what he read. Ellis and I got this *County Republican* sometimes and, skipping all the big words, we concluded that the whole country was going to smash over something called politics.

Lige didn't vote, nor did I ever hear of any other man doing it. Took an all-day trip, and nobody cared. Politics was another mystery far off, incomprehensible like God and the Devil and the Law; don't go monkeying with 'em.

In September, with the ripening corn, and the drought parching the pastures dry and hot, Ellis and I had to ride fence to keep the loose stock out of the fields. Mr. Gebauer and the Rooshins had strong fences, but Lige's were of old rusty wire and rotted little posts, and a range steer would just stick his head through and keep going. Until the corn was out of the fields Ellis and I had a time of it. We rode the old retired farm team out to the far north section line, carrying the rusty wire stretcher, a hammer and a pocket of staples, hunting the broken strands, twisting them to a splice and then trying to haul the wire tight but not too tight. If you did that, you might have a broken wire whizzing around your ears.

There was never a fence-riding day that we didn't come home with bloody cuts from the barbs, but we wouldn't let anyone see them. You could cut an Indian worse than that and he wouldn't holler, so we wouldn't holler. But far off on the section line where Effie couldn't hear we could swear loud as we pleased, no dangs and darns as we used at the house but real good cusswords. We hated barbed wire as much as the cowhands had when the farmers took over the land. Our young stock was forever getting frightfully cut on the fences as they didn't know what wire was. Lige had to shoot two colts who nearly gutted themselves. Cows learned quicker and were cautious.

Well, this hot morning we had found but one break, and we drove what wandering steers were about the fence some miles north from the corn. I sat on my cornhusk-sack saddle and wished there was some shade within two miles. Old Tops also was droopy-eared with the heat.

Ellis came back on Jewel. He said, "Say, you know what? We got this far up here North an' that Railroad can't be much farther. Let's go hunt it."

"Yeh. See if Lige is tellin' truth about a train goin' so fast it would scare us."

"Wouldn't scare me, not with Jewel to pull out on."

"Me either. But I couldn't move Tops off a walk no matter how scared I was. It's a good time anyhow to explore North Road. We said we would next after West Road. An' found them pore Indians."

Indians and Out West had been a big disappointment. Maybe Up North would have something better. We'd go a piece on this prairie and discover something sure. Eskimos must be pretty dang far away, hot as it was today on North Road—just a prairie trail like all our roads leading to Mystery.

All a hot day we ambled along faint wagon tracks in the dried grass. Tumbleweeds were big now, higher than my head, and a good place for Indians, but there weren't any. We'd start with a passel of bread and fried pork, stuff that we could carry easy in a piece of paper down inside our shirts. But it always worked out, and we got pretty greasy by the time we ate. I didn't get off my horse, for it was a job climbing his legs and neck again out here with nothing to get a boost on.

We passed the Rooshin settlement and saw women in black shawls working in the fields. Americans wouldn't do that; maybe that was why the foreign folks had better farms. We came upon one sod house with stock in the corral and turned in for a drink with the horses at the windmill trough. Then we went to the soddy and yelled. Nobody was home. The door wide open and everything inside well kept. But the owners weren't within miles. That's the way it was in that country. Nobody locked their houses. Lige didn't have a lock on his ranch. I never heard of a house being robbed either until I grew up and went Back East—to Wisconsin, where folks had that mysterious thing which Effie called Culture. Then people had to lock themselves in nights, and it seemed strange to me.

Well, this hot autumn day we rode on, hunting that Railroad. Late in the afternoon we were thirsty again, and when we saw taller grass which would mean a slough we headed for it. But we found nothing but dry cracked muddy bottom, and up this we kicked the tired old horses. Ellis was always ahead of me, for Jewel was the best animal. He was far ahead of me around the biggest grass when he began to yell. I turned Ol' Tops that way, for it must mean water. But when I passed the slough grass, there was the Railroad. I knew it the first look from a picture in the Joggerfee book. So we both began yelling and rode closer.

"Boy, look at that! Them's rails to keep a train on the track!"

We slid off the horses and climbed a low yellow bank of dirt and felt of the iron rails excitedly. The rails ran straight Back East and Out West into the sunset. We sat on them and kept on yelling with delight.

"Chick, we got somethin' to brag about now! Railroad!"

"Headed for Californy! Boy, this is the biggest thing we see yet!"

The sun was low and red, and the silence was something to scare you. I sat on a hot rail and seemed to feel something. Then I put my ear down to it. There was a faint humming in the iron, and while I listened Ellis jumped up and yelled, " 'Way off east yander—smoke! That's an engine for a fact. Just like Lige said an engine was—smoke!"

We stared until we saw a dot in the east and it moved. The humming was louder and louder. The dot grew bigger and bigger with more smoke, and pretty soon there was a long streak of smoke and more noise than I'd ever heard in my life.

Ellis yelled again, "Git out o' here! She's comin'!"

He ran for the horses, and I followed him when that thing got too close. A long yellow train went past with mighty howls and clanks. When we got to the draw I saw the critters heading south, Ol' Tops legging faster than he'd done in ten years. But we felt safe now. That yellow thing had whirled on and on, howling at us until it was just a dot against the red in the west.

"Headin' to Californy, I bet. Wish Effie was here—she always hankerin' fer Californy. Wish I was on that train."

"Not me! Too fast, just like Lige said. An' suppose the durn thing jumped off them little rails an' took after a man, fast like that? I was sure skairt."

"I wasn't skairt, but I wouldn't want to live near that train, all the fuss it makes. Where's Ol' Tops?"

The two horses were still going south—far south. It was too much excitement for them. We followed half a mile, and Ellis said it was my fault leaving the animals. Well, no use complaining. We headed back for the Railroad and followed the rails westward, hoping to find water and a place to bed down, for tonight was going to be September-cool. It was nearly dark when we came to a little gully with a bridge across it.

That was also a sight to see. We walked across the ties and down under it, and, sure enough, in the lowest sandy spot was a little seep of water. We scooped it out and got a drink with mud and grass in it. Then I looked up. There was a rope hanging from the bridge with a loop at the end, an old rope, dry and twisty as if it had been there a long time. Rope was a scarce thing at Lige's and the Buffalo Waller. I went up on the bridge and untied it after a long job, prying the knot with my toad stabber.

Ellis got it below, and then he called up to me, "Say, down this gully there's a house. Just a little small house with big weeds all around it. Nobody home, but we could bed down there outa the wind mebbe till mornin', for we got to leg home with nothin' to eat."

We went down the draw, watching every way cautiously. The place sure was scary. Just a wooden shack on the side of the draw in the weeds. Somebody must have tried to make a garden, but a long time ago. The door was open, but it was too dark to see much. I felt a rusty old iron bed. And a lot of old dried newspapers, all stuck together from wet sometime. Anyhow they'd do for cover. It was so dark now we had to feel around, but we lay on the springs and pulled the stiff papers over us.

When the first daylight came we saw around us. Just a little frame shack with one window and a dirt floor. But somebody had tried to make it like home. There was a shelf with a dusty lamp on it and a little table made of boxes. These and the rusty bed were all that were in the place. Somebody had tried to paste newspaper on the walls, but it was all loose, hanging in strips, hard and dry, and in places were dark stains where water must have seeped through the roof and streaked it. We went out and walked around, pretty hungry, and drank some slough water.

Down the draw in the dead weed patch there were little stakes as if someone had tried to fence in a garden piece. And beyond that in the prairie grass was a little mound with a little wooden cross leaning from it.

We walked around cautiously. We'd never seen a grave, but this was surely one. Little weedy mound you'd hardly see.

"Must been a baby-kid, about as big as Gebauer's littlest one," said Ellis.

"Little kid died an' the folks pulled up stakes an' left their homestead. Nobody been here for years."

We hung around awhile, feeling quiet. Nobody around our section had ever died that we knew of. Nor were born either, not any folks we heard about. Ellis had pulled some weeds from the grave, and I straightened the cross, but it busted off. I jammed it tighter. So baby-kids died, did they? Like chickens and little pigs and calves? We went back to the shack and cleared more mud from the drinking hole. The mystery of life was again on our minds, but now the sun was up over the east prairie.

Ellis said, "Well, we better pull out. I'm sure hungry."

"We'll take that ol' rope, fer if it's too rotten for Lige we can use it at the Waller to hang things on. I'm goin' to roll up some of them old papers too fer Effie to read mebbe. You can see some letters even if they are all stained up."

I tore the best ones from the wall and rolled them into a stiff bundle. They must have been big-city papers, for we could spell out St. Louis and we knew that was Back East. Then I saw some little lines in a corner and spelled them out also.

Ellis had started with the old rope. He wasn't interested in what words and letters said. But I waited a moment with the bundle of papers. The lines were mostly little words, and I slowly spelled them, blowing the dust away.

> "In the Heart of the Hills of Life, I know
> Two springs that with unbroken flow
> Forever pour their lucent streams
> Into my soul's far Lake of Dreams."

I couldn't read more because of the dark stains. But I went on with the paper bundle, thinking of the words. What was that? What did they mean? Hills of Life? . . . Lake of Dreams?

All a mystery again. The first bit of poetry I ever saw

or heard. A great many years later I found it was Lanier's. Now I walked on, repeating it, but didn't know why. Maybe just pretty. Words. Part of Mystery. I'd never seen a hill or a lake, but Lige and Effie had, and they said they were fine big things. Someday, beyond the rim of our known little world we would see them. Would we?

We started to walk south from the railroad culvert and passed the little grave again. Ellis said, "Looks like everybody forgot this baby-kid. Pretty soon you won't see it's a grave. Go git that busted shovel from the shack an' we'll build it up higher. Then folks goin' by on the train can see it."

I got the shovel, and we started work. While I heaped up dirt Ellis dragged some old railroad ties from near the track, and we strung them around in a sort of fence with all the weeds pulled from inside around the fresh mound.

It was pretty dang hot, and we couldn't get any water out of the mudhole this morning. We hadn't eaten since yesterday noon, and it would be a long trip home on foot in the sun. We didn't say much, working around the grave, but before we left it Ellis said, "Say, I heard tell that when you have a dead person you put a whole lot o' flowers around him."

"There's some old ragged sunflowers back o' the shack. We'll fetch 'em. Come on, afore we feel too tired to wiggle."

We dragged the dusty broken sunflower stalks over the grave, the faded flowers on top, and then started home. Had to walk for hours before we saw the first soddy away off by a brown cornfield which was a guide to our section. Then we saw the Rooshin settlement and passed it a mile away. By sundown we were pretty well played out. When we made it to Lige's place we stumbled to the horse trough and shoved the critters away. We drank and drank and wiped dusty sweat away and grinned again. Then on to the sod house, yelling as usual when we came in from anywhere.

The folks were all through eating. Effie was washing dishes. Lige was studying his old almanac again. We yelled, "Looky what we got! Lot o' old papers an' a piece o' rope!"

Lige said, as usual, "Where in tunket you boys been all day an' night? Sometime you'll git in trouble an' won't git back. The horses came home alone, worried me."

"Oh, let 'em run free!" Effie cried. "Wherever they want, run free. Land, I wish I could go traipsin' off somewhere!"

"We discovered the Railroad and saw a train whizzin'. And, looky, a rope. It was hangin' to a bridge. An' we found a little baby-kid's grave where some homesteader'd lived."

"Bridge?" Lige looked queerly at me. "Rope? Little shack in a gully where was water? I been there once myself." He got up slowly and looked at the rope on the floor. He looked at the bundle of stiff papers with black stains on them.

"Aw, we didn't steal that rope. Nobody'd want it."

"No, I guess not," Lige said. "Look here, you dang fools. That rope's been hung to that culvert for eight years or more fer a warnin'. Nobody'd take it down. That's where the last cattlemen hung a feller named Wilson. He lived in that shack. He was a rustler, they said, an' a bad man. He killed his wife too, right in that shack on that bed when he was cornered. But I guess them cow riders hung him for stealin' stock, which was considered worst in them days."

Effie said, "You boys git that hanged man's rope outa my house! Chick, you quit stickin' yore head through that noose! Land, what next?"

I didn't see what there was to get excited about. But I tried to change the subject. I spread the old stiff papers. "Look what we got fer you, Effie. Stuff to read mebbe!"

Lige got up and looked closely. "Out that man's shack, hey?"

"Yeh. We pulled 'em off the wall to sleep under on that ol' bed."

"Yeh, I guess," said Lige. "That's where Wilson killed his woman with an ax—on that bed. I was in there year or two later. Them newspapers the woman had pasted on the wall—tryin' to make it homelike, I guess—they was all splattered with blood. Look, now!"

We stared at the dark stains. Effie didn't wait. She got her broom and yelled, "Git all that stuff outa my house! Lige, you burn it up tomorry!"

"Hell, no!" I said. "It's got stuff on it to read. I'll give them papers to Teacher, an' mebbe Miss Worsenever."

"No, you don't! Get that stuff outa here. Hanged man's rope an' you wearin' it round your neck!"

"Didn't hurt me."

"Wonder you boys didn't see a ghost," said Lige.

"Aw, we slept fine. This mornin' we found a baby-kid's grave an' cleaned weeds off it. Musta been little-bitty tyke."

"Yeh," said Lige. "I remember that too. There was a

little grave beyond the garden. Child died a year afore they hanged Wilson. Nobody ever goes there much any more after the cow riders hanged him an' sheriff took him down from that rope. But they left the rope fer warnin'.''

Lige looked dang solemn. Ellis and I lugged the stuff out.

Ellis said, "Ma, we ain't had a thing to eat since yesterday."

Effie warmed the coffee and got plates. "Land, what next? You boys'll git me in a state o' mind someday."

Well, we didn't burn the hanged man's rope. Next day we took it and the papers with old blood on them out to the Waller and put them away with all the plunder we had hidden there.

Ellis said, "I'm dang glad we cleaned the baby-kid's grave."

"Yeh, me too. Lige said it was a little boy, an' when he died his mother buried him all by herself, nobody to help her, fer her man was an outlaw an' off somewhere stealin' horses when the little boy died. Well, I'm glad we fixed up that grave. Mebbe folks'll remember that a boy lived there once."

"Yeh, folks on trains goin' to Californy can see the fence an' the grave an' wonder who it was. Won't know his dad was ever hanged. Ner mother got killed. Just see a little grave."

Thirty years later travelers could see the little grave. For the railroad section hands, when they saw what we had done, kept the old tie fence up and the mound cleared. But nobody remembered then about the hanged man's son who was buried there.

# 8

# The Mysterious Murder of
# Marion Marlow

---

Earl Staley came riding in another time with his two pack animals, and the whole outfit was ganted up and dusty. Earl was getting more mysterious than ever. Lige said he was batchin' over westward, trying to file for a claim. Marion hadn't been to see us for weeks, and the queer thing was that Earl never asked about him. Earl was just tuckered out.

Effie said, "Well, the man has to come back here an' eat sometimes, I guess. He aims to quit cow business an' grow up with the country."

I didn't think so. That one day of farmwork, helping me stack straw, had settled him. But when Lige was putting in winter wheat Earl used to ride around behind and watch. Some nights he'd ride down to Gebauer's and maybe try to talk to that German girl. I got to thinking one time what ailed Earl on his mind; and once when I asked him again where Marion Marlow had gone so suddenly he just stared and didn't answer. Nobody knew about Marlow any more.

One day Ellis and I were out in the South Eighty stubble with the dogs digging gophers out their holes, and I saw a lot of buzzards circling about over Mr. Gebauer's big corn beyond our Eighty. Ellis said there must be a dead cow over there for buzzards. We traipsed down to see if it was any of Lige's stock, and there wasn't any to be found. But the buzzards kept on circling ahead. The dogs picked up a trail, and I went along down a corn row to a little gully where the field ended. Then I found an old torn hat, and that was queer. Old hat out there.

I said, "Looks like the hat Marion wore before he went to Mexico an' got all duded up."

Ellis kicked the old hat into the gully. But it got me to thinking of that man Wilson who got hanged to the railroad bridge for cattle rustlin'. Maybe Marion got hanged too.

But there wasn't a tree or anything down here to hang a man to. Maybe he was shot and laying around somewhere, all the buzzards circling over south ahead of us. I didn't tell Ellis, but I began to think it over. Effie said in the book two fellers was fighting over a girl and it was exciting. And she was egging Earl on to go sparking Miss Worsenever and acting mysterious, and Marion just vanished without a word. Didn't make sense, except that the two gets in a fight and Earl shoots him.

I went back with Ellis to the ranch, thinking that when I could get away alone I'd go hunt for Marion if he hadn't been entirely eat up by buzzards. Ought to be some bones anyhow. I didn't tell anybody. I just watched Earl close. Ellis had to go out to the North Eighty and help Lige with his seeder, working it by hand, for the machine jigger that ran it wouldn't work. Just rusted out like Lige's wire fence. Some cattle were grazing down near the east cornfield and it was a boy's job to watch that fence. So I took the stretcher and staples and got on Ol' Tops and rode down the corn rows, and, sure enough, at the end some steers were shoving through the wires. I herded 'em back and then figured I'd better tackle that fence so I wouldn't have to ride the line all afternoon.

Then I saw Earl riding off back of the corn, and maybe he'd help. Stretching wire was a two-man job, one to stretch and the other to hammer staples in the posts. But Earl didn't come near me when I slid off Tops and hitched the busted wire to the stretcher. That cowhand would just laze around out there on the prairie on his pony, watching the cattle. He hated barbed wire like all cowmen did, but there were too many settlers around here now for cowmen to raise a fuss about fences as they did years ago.

And there he sat, easy, not sweating a hair, and me hauling on that wire after I twisted a splice in it with the nippers. No farmwork for them cowhands if they could help it! It made me pretty mad, and I began to cuss the wire and jerk on the stretcher to show that feller I could do a man's work if he couldn't. I got a wire tight and stapled it to one of Lige's crazy board posts, then untangled another twisted coil and laid it straight. Earl didn't come near. No cowhand would ever bring a horse near wire, for their outfits weren't used to it, and if wire broke under the stretcher it would whirl any-which-way. Well, I was hot and sweaty and mad, and I was going to show off to a lazy cowhand. So I hauled on that wire hard, tighter and tighter, and tried to sing to show Earl I didn't care a whoop what he done. I was too dignified to speak to him.

Then the rusty wire broke at the splice. I got loose of
my end and ran, but back it came, looping fast, and I
hadn't got a yard away when a coil caught me—around the
pants—and another coil tightened around my shoulders. It
jerked me down, and I just lay there, thinking about it.
I was trapped like a rabbit in a snare. I couldn't move my
arms, but I didn't try. Didn't want that cowhand to see
me all snarled up in wire. Blood was streakin' down my
shirt, and it hurt in a lot of places where barbs tore into
my hide. But I didn't yell; Indians could stand worse than
that and not yell. Then I heard an animal come up.

There was Earl staring down at me. Then he said, "You
hurt? Why didn't you holler?"

"Who? Me? I ain't a hand to holler. You go chase
cows."

He got off his pony an' came over. "You didn't have
any call to go foolin' with that damned wire alone. Two-
man job, stretchin' fence."

"I'm all right. I can get outa this in no time."

He looked me all over. "You couldn't wiggle a foot.
Yore wropped tight."

He knelt down and pulled a wire. It hurt me all over,
but I wouldn't yell. I said, "Don't worry about me. I can
get loose."

"No, you can't. You'd die bleedin' out here on the
prairie."

"Yeh, mebbe. Mebbe like ol' Marion, who disappeared
somehow, mebbe dead."

Earl looked startled. "Who told you that?"

"Neve' mind—neve' mind. You ain't foolin' me!"

He didn't say anything for a while. Just worked to

loosen the wire coil, and every time he moved a barb it hurt. But I figured how you could shoot an Indian full of arrows and he'd just sneer, so I tried to sneer at Earl but didn't know how. He got the other coil from my legs, and I crawled up. "You cut in six places bad. You dang smarty, hold still." He peeled down my pants and chewed his wad of tobacco and slapped it on a cut.

I said, "I don't need doctorin'. I'll git Tops an' git home."

"Yore plug heard that wire larrup, an' he went home. I'm totin' you in to Effie on a real cayuse." He chewed up more spit and plug cut and slapped it on my legs. It hurt. "Yell, you little devil! Yell! Don't kick, bleedin' like this. Effie can fix it up."

He slapped me across his pony in front like I was a sack of meal. Then he loped to the soddy, holding me by what was left of the seat of my breeches. Then he yelled to Effie, "Well, here's yore busted-up farmer! Stop kickin', you piece o' rawhide!"

Effie took one look and ran back in. Then she came out with the jar of Carbolic Acid Salve, Good for Man and Beast. She slapped some on. Then Lige came in for all the commotion. He got a handful of axle grease and lathered my legs. Then Ellis got some tar they keep to slap on horses when they get cut. That stuff hurt like all git out. But I didn't yell. All I wanted was a swig of Piso's Pain Killer, Good for Consumption, and Effie said, "No, you don't. Tastes like whisky, that's why you want it."

Lige said, "Hell, woman, give him a swig! He's bleedin'!"

"No, you don't. Keep out o' my trunk, all o' you. I'll be mad!"

Well, I crawled up soon as they all took hands off me.

Effie hollered at Lige, "Don't you know better 'n send this boy out alone stretchin' yore rusty ol' wire?"

"I didn't send him. The smarty just goes off on his own."

"If Earl hadn't found him, he'd been clean dead by now."

This made me mad too. I hollered, "I wasn't half dead! I'd got out them wires alone, just give me time."

"You'd bled white by now. You oughta thank Earl."

"Naw, I ain't goin' to thank anybody. I don't want doctorin'. Just lemme alone."

Well, I limped off and tried to sit in the shade of the soddy, the only shade we had and it wasn't much. But Effie had a bolt of blue jeans spread out there, for she'd been whacking out some breeches for Ellis and me. She knelt down on it and spread my old torn pants on the cloth and whacked away with her shears and just gave me a quiet look now and then. Ol' Effie knew better 'n pester a man when he was gritting his teeth to be like an Indian when you torture him. If any of 'em had laid another hand on me, I'd certainly have sneered at 'em.

Lige went back to his work and to a mighty hot day. Earl rode off south. I'd got him uneasy, asking about Marion Marlow, who must have been shot and buried out there beyond South Eighty. He looked scared any time you talked about Marion now. Soon as my cuts healed I intended to go discover something: who killed Marlow anyhow? But I was sore for a week. I could wash all that stuff—axle grease and carbolic and plug tobacco—off my legs, but not that tar Ellis rubbed on me. The stuff stuck black and hard. But I could sneak away down South Eighty through the big corn rows to see what the buzzards was jerking around in the big gully.

It was mysterious. But a lot of things were getting mysterious. Earl coming and going; if he was taking up land out in Custer County, he'd come a good many miles just to eat Effie's cooking once in a while. His two pack critters always seemed strapped around bigger with stuff than I'd ever seen when he used to pull out for Texas if he smelled farmwork. In the soddy Effie didn't seem to have so many pots and lids hanging behind the stove. There used to be an old busted rocking chair she sat in every so often in the shade of the house. Ellis and I always got the old broken kitchen stuff to lug out to the Waller, and we hoped sometime Effie's rocker would bust completely and then we'd have it to furnish our dugout. Suddenly the durn thing was gone. The morning Earl went away Lige was hitching up and singing:

"Snakes in his whisky, frawgs in his beer,
The ol' man died with a rag in his ear,
The rag fell out, an' the wind blew in
An' the old man took to drink agin!"

Effie came out and saw Earl packed up. She said to me, "Why don't you ever thank Earl for pawin' you out that bobbed wire, like a polite gentleman?"

Well, I'd never said thank you to anybody yet. But I went to the road and yelled, "Much obliged!"

Earl yelled back, "Yours truly!"

I yelled, "Much obliged!"

He yelled, "Yours respectfully!" And off he clatters with his pack animals heading Out West. Earl was perkin' up; he never codded me before; just a solemn serious cuss. But he was full of good cooking again and felt hearty.

September was the hot dry month. I limped around, scraping scabs off my legs. I could hardly wear breeches for that tar still sticking fast. Well, Effie was making us new school clothes, but I told her no use, they'd just stick fast to me. She kept on whacking the blue jeans and pushing back her hair, all sweaty, for it was hard to keep out of the sun. She held a hoe handle up to measure me for a wamus. Everything Effie made for us was cut square and baggy. When she got a lot of pieces cut out she'd take them into the house to her little sewing machine. The louder it rattled the louder she'd sing:

> "Hi-me-ho fer Lucy, oh!
> Bonny, bonny Lucy, oh!
> Give this world an' all I know
> For bonny, bonny Lucy, oh!"

New duds were stiff and scratchy. Ellis and I always took our wamuses out to the Buffalo Waller and pounded them with the old shotgun barrel to get them to fit comfortable.

Lige come in early from fall plowing. He said it was too dang hot. He bet a hundred and ten. He wouldn't push a team today. Nobody around there ever knew how hot it was. Nobody had a thermometer. Had to hear in town maybe a month later how hot it was. No one had scales either except the German, so nobody ever knew how much anything weighed. If any wagonman came by heading west and wanted to buy potatoes or wheat or anything, or meat if it was butchering time, Lige would just shovel a lot into the man's wagon. He had beef by the chunk, and a big chunk. Then when the emigrant wanted to pay, Lige would scratch his head and say, "Hell, no! I ain't ever charged fer anything to eat yet. I was first man settled around here, an' sometimes Effie an' I was hungry, no first-breakin' corn or a meat critter. Keep yore money, friend."

No wonder the dang fool had such a time with a Mortgage and I never got a Third Reader.

That day was too hot for the dogs to follow us out to the Waller. We got down in the dugout from the sun. I was picking more scabs off my legs around the spots of tar when Ellis turned from watching out of the dugout over the rim of the Waller. Not a cloud in the brassy sky, fields dried and burned. Even the birds and coyotes and jack rabbits had pulled out south for the creek timber country, I guess.

Ellis said, "But it ain't too hot fer buzzards. Look over south, there's more than ever. Some stock drought-dead, mebbe."

I looked mysterious like Earl had been doing. "Ain't cows. It's a dead feller. Marion Marlow, that's what. Earl an' Marion had a big fight over that German girl, an' Earl won gun-shootin'. So he buried pore ol' Marion in that draw, an' now the coyotes dug him out an' the buzzards smelled him an' come hell-whoopin' fer miles."

Ellis' eyes stuck out big. "How you know?"

"Oh, I know. Stands to reason. Marion vanished an'

Earl actin' queer. Effie queer too. She won't tell nothin', fer this year she likes Earl after naggin' about him two winters, boardin' in on us fer chores an' then just playin' seven-up with Lige every night."

Ellis got up on the Waller rim and stared. I went out too. Certainly more buzzards. I said, "That's it. Effie won't betray Earl because she aims to git him married an' start homesteadin'. Like in a book, forgive a feller an' reform him. Then he gits the girl."

"Yeh? Chick, you do figger things out. Let's go peruse down that draw afore buzzards settle. We can spot 'em now in the air."

"We'll find him all right. Pore ol' Marion, he never meant any harm! Just a devilin' wild cuss. Earl, he's steady. But you go to grab a man's girl an' shootin' starts."

"I don't see how it happens. Earl never seemed like a man that'd want any girl anyhow, let alone shootin' about her."

"He didn't want a girl till Effie got him all tangled up. Hey, I bet that's where her busted rocker went! An' pots an' pans an' stuff out the house. She's givin' it to Earl, an' he's sneakin' it out to Custer County fer his soddy."

"I always aimed we'd get the rocker fer out here. Well, Chick, mebbe you figgered it out. You got more sense 'n anybody even if it's all wrong, like Teacher says when you stand up an' start argyin'."

"Well, come on. Let's trail them buzzards afore too dark."

So off we legged—first into South Eighty corn along a down row Lige already had made fer husking, and was it hot! Big high corn is the hottest place to be ever. We were glad to come out on the south line and then along the gully through big dry grass. Then we rounded a turn and saw some buzzards, but they were always a mile off, it looked. We went on and at last saw one on the ground. He flew away, and I went on ahead to a water-dry place, the dust all cracked. Then I saw it and turned around to Ellis.

"What'd I tell yeh? Bones all scratched around outa the ground."

Ellis came nearer, but not where I was. He could see a bone half out the ground in the side of the gully. He said, "Well, for Pete's sake, don't touch it! We got to head home an' tell Lige this. It's a case fer sheriffs."

"I don't want no dang sheriffs messin' in. Never seen a sheriff yet an' don't aim ever to see one. Sheriffs make more trouble than anybody livin', Lige says."

"Well, what we do, then?"

"Git hold o' Earl when he comes back an' make him confess."

"Effie'll tan yore hide if you go to makin' trouble fer Earl."

"Naw, she won't. She wants things excitin'."


On hot bad days Ellis and I would get close to the sod wall, only shade we could find, and mix sody water. Get some water from the windmill tank, and it was almost hot too, then put in some vinegar and sugar and then a spoonful of sody from Effie's can. You had to drink it quick while it fizzled or else all you had was warm water with vinegar in it. Then we'd take a bucketful out to Lige, along with the sody can. We'd dump sody in quick and Lige would swallow it quick.

Lige was always glad to stop and talk. He wouldn't see a man maybe in two weeks, for no wagon folks passed any more. And he had to rest his team a lot. We'd all squat in the hot sun and drink sody out the bucket. I still couldn't sit down easy on account of tar in my cuts.

Lige said, "Miss Frawleen an' Gebauer stopped last night after you boys were asleep to ask how you was. Far as I could make out, she'd been a nurse in the Old Country, an' she'd got some good stuff to heal you up fer school."

"I don't want any German stuff on top o' this tar. And, long as I got sores, I won't have to go to school. An' that Teacher'll holler about me bein' in Second Reader when I know as much as I do. Teachers always say that."

"Don't go actin' smart with 'em." He looked far off and rubbed his thin whiskers. "Come Christmas I'm goin' to git you a new readin' book. Damn if I don't, if I have to go without tobaccy."

"Don't need any."

"Yeh," Ellis jeered. "That's so he don't have to study, knowin' so much already."

"Little learnin' don't hurt anybody," said Lige. "Now, back in West Virginny I never got far as you are. Had to go breaker-boy in coal mines."

"'Way underground?" said Ellis. "Like a man was buried?"

"Yes-sir-bobbee! Underground!"

Well, that started me thinking again about the bones and buzzards out over that prairie draw. I said, "If you found a dead feller, what'd you do?"

"Wouldn't do a dang thing. Let him alone."

Ellis said, "Wouldn't you have to tell a sheriff?"

"I guess not. We don't want any sheriff messin' around out in our end o' the county."

Well, that sounded pretty good; we could trust Lige. So I said, "Looky, we got a dead feller, an' I bet I know who it is!"

Lige just looked dumb at me. "Now what's this talk?"

"Found his bones stickin' out where the coyotes had been diggin'. Know who he is too. Just stands to reason."

"Well, I'm fitchered!" said Lige. "Hell-a-mile! How come?"

So I told him, with Ellis putting in a word but looking mighty scared. Lige listened and then said, "Found a hat too, right near there? Marion Marlow's hat?"

"Well, it wasn't his new fancy Mexican hat what he came back in. Just an ol' hat laid in dirt for months, I guess."

"Coyotes musta dragged his hat," said Ellis. "But we found bones too, stickin' out the bank!"

"How do you know they was Marion's bones?"

"Just stands to reason," I said. "Earl an' Marion had a row about Miss Frawleen an' Earl shoots first. In the book——"

"Dang the book! I'll go see that busted grave. I won't touch any bones, though. Mebbe I'll cover 'em up better."

"Nobody ought to go messin' around about any gun fight," I said. "Earl's suspicious already I know somethin'."

"Earl does act mighty funny these days," Lige said. "But I don't figger him a gun-fightin' cowhand. Peaceable, quiet man."

"Yeh? Effie'd tell you! Them's the kind to look out for when you rile 'em! An' when one man's tryin' to grab another man's girl, then it's all right to shoot. Kill 'em dead!"

Lige chewed his chin whiskers. "Yeh, they been cases like that. Yeh, many a man's dead an' buried fightin' about women. Well, I guess we better not do anything. Ain't our fight."

He drank the rest of the sody water and started his team. Ellis and I went back to the ranch. Ellis said, "Say, you oughtn't told Lige about this shootin'. Now he'll be worried all fall, an' when Lige gits somethin' on his mind Effie always makes him spit it out. You oughtn't to trust nobody, Chick. But Lige is a fair-minded codger. Effie laughs about everything, but when she knows this she won't laugh. She never gave us a lickin' yet, but she'll tan you now sure!"

"Not while I got sores on my legs she won't." I didn't say any more. Now Ellis was worried. I wasn't worried; never was a hand to worry about dead folks or anything. Well, Lige didn't ask us any more questions. He went down, thinking I didn't know it, and looked at Marion's bones sticking out the gully bank, but he didn't go near. Just came back studying. He whispered to me, "Chick, a thing like this drives a man to drink."

"Me too. If Earl was back, mebbe we could swipe some whisky if he had any. But he don't seem drinkin' since Effie got him all worked up about homesteadin' in Custer County."

"You let whisky alone, you sawed-off smarty."

I didn't tell him any more. Lige was a man who didn't

even want to think about trouble, so he dodged it. He was
hauling wheat to town, a day-and-night trip, and we knew
he'd had a drink one trip. He wasn't a real drinking man,
and Effie never nagged him about it. But I knew he was
worried now about Marion.

We had to thresh the beans before a rain. That was another dusty job boys got and also got full of scratchy stickers. We flailed the white beans on a horse blanket, tossed
them up into the wind from a bucket to blow the chaff,
and sacked them up and dragged them to the soddy. More
beans than any family could use in a year, and the rest were
left to sprout and rot. We flailed the buckwheat too, for
hot cakes next winter.

Lige came home once with a whole barrel of moldy dried
apples, and what for nobody knew. Must have had a drink
that trip. Ellis and I spent a day picking the bad ones out,
and Effie started to make dried-apple pie, which was the
only fruit we had. Pies all over the soddy, and then Ellis
and I had to ride around for miles giving pies to people.
I suppose those thrifty foreign folks thought Americans
were crazy. Anyhow Lige's folks. He paid a dollar for
the bad dried apples which should have gone toward the
Mortgage. But Effie laughed, and I rode ol' shaggy Tops
to houses whose people I didn't know and yelled, "Pie!"
When a woman came out of her soddy I shoved a pie down
to her, wrapped in a piece of newspaper. It dripped on her,
and Tops and I were smeared up with pie juice dripping
from the basket. I yelled "Pie!" again and rode off. I wonder what people thought?

Once Lige came from town very late and woke us all
up with his shouts from the wagon. Ellis and I slid out

from under the old buffalo skin under the wagon and shivered, standing in our shirts which were the only sleeping gowns we ever had. Effie stuck her head out of the soddy door. Lige whooped, "I got it! This time I got it!" He went in. "Git the boys up quick! Yes-sir-bobbee, I got it this time!"

"Now what? More dried apples or what?"

He yelled at me across the oilclothed table, "Here y'are, Chick! She's a dinger! Bigger book 'n anybody's got."

Effie was unwrapping a newspaper package. "My land, yes!"

"I been askin' the boys around Jake's fer a long time did anybody have a readin' book fer Chick. Ol' cowman from down near Kansas line gimme this what used to belong to his sister. Now Chick can brag at school, hell-bent fer education!"

"Some ol' whisky-head's reader?" said Effie. "Look, Chick."

I opened the thing to a whole page of little fine words. Whole book of 'em, so heavy I could hardly lug it. Effie turned to the first page. I got behind Lige where I didn't have to see it. Effie hauled me out where I had to see my book. Then she said, "This says, well, it spells D-I-C-T-I-O-N-A-R-Y!"

"Whoop!" Lige yelled. "I knew she was a buster!"

"Dictionary," said Effie. "I know what this is. But it'll just worry his brains now. He wants a Third Reader just. Land, what next? Chick with a dictionary!"

"Ain't goin' to worry me none. I can just lug it around."

Effie's eyes sparkled. "Sure! An' study it. Read it hard!"

Lige felt so flattered he'd done something to please Effie

that he tickled her neck. "You bet! This will jump Chick away head of everybody in that cussed school. I'll tell all the boys around Jake's place now we got Chick started hell-fer-leather-educated."

Ellis looked pretty jealous. He pawed over some pages and grunted, "This book's no good. Ain't a line makes sense to me."

"Well, I won't start right away with it in school. I'll keep it out at the Buffalo Waller an' kinda git used to it."

"You take it right to school an' show 'em!" Lige roared. "I bet Teacher don't know half in that book! It's a buster!"

"I bet Miss Frawleen don't know a dang thing in my book. I bet they don't have 'em like this in Germany. Dick—dick——"

"Git to bed, everybody," said Effie. "Lands, it's late! An' the clock's stopped somehow!"

Lige said, "Big night like this, let 'er stop. What's a dang clock fer anyhow?"

So we all went to bed. Lige was singing the last I heard. Clock? What for anybody have a clock? Who ever cared what time it was at Lige's place? Nobody.

Lige was happy the next morning, singing while he hitched up.

Ellis and I were out on the West Eighty digging gophers from the sod, all the dogs helping. I had a good excuse for not going back to school with the big dictionary. My legs were still scabby from the tar, and if I'd pick the sores a little they'd stay raw, and we didn't have to start school again where I'd have to sit still so long that pants hurt. I had my head down in the hole, forking with a stick for a gopher, when Ellis yelled, "What ails Lige now, lopin' so fast? Left his plow right in the furrow an' run!"

Lige came on a lope, and he was excited bad. Just yelled to me, "Now you done it! Now you raised conniption hell!"

"What I done?"

"Sheriff's at the ranch an' wants the boy that found Marion Marlow's bones!"

"How any sheriff know I found any bones?"

Ellis shrieked, "Now you done it, now you done it! Bones!"

The dogs began to bark, and I stuttered, "Don't go p-pickin' on me about nothin'. Sheriff don't want me—he d-don't even know me."

"That's it," gasped Lige. "He does. Yore the boy that found dead man's bones. He's come investigatin'."

Well, I looked away at the ranch buildings dancing in the heat. There was a rig by the soddy that beat Gebauer's buggy all hollow. This had two horses and two seats and a square top with little fringe all around. All shiny-black and fine. And Effie was out talking to a big man with a whip in the front seat.

"Well, how he know he wants me?" I said.

Lige was pained some. He said, "Well, it's like this. I went to town with load o' wheat an' got a drink an' then met a feller from county seat an' got to braggin', I reckon. I said out home we had couple o' smart boys who could run down any murder feller. Talked and talked, I guess—too much. Well, now it seems this feller was in the courthouse workin' an' he talked. Come to sheriff's ears, an' now out he boils to see you, Chick."

Ellis said, "You better run! Law after you now!"

I looked all around. There wasn't a place to run out of sight nearer than the Rooshins' three miles north. Except the Waller over west'ard. I didn't wait. Started full-lope for the Waller. Ellis was behind when his pa called him. He and Lige went back to the ranch kind of slow to give me time to hide up, I guess. But, dang it, when I got to the Waller and turned to look, that big buggy with the tassels was coming on West Road, and the sheriff had picked up Lige and Ellis and there was four dogs trailing along. I didn't have no more chance than a pup fighting a polecat.

But I climbed down and into the dugout. I had the muskit there but no powder. Other old guns were no good at all. Anyhow, in a minute I'd be surrounded, so I sat down to wait 'em.

That shiny rig left the road and bumped across the prairie and stopped. The sheriff was a big man with a big mustache and a star on his galluses. He pointed his whip at Ellis. "That the one who saw this dead man stickin' out the ground?"

Ellis looked mighty pale. Lige was in fidgets. Wouldn't talk.

Then Ellis said, his words kinda pale too, "Mister, I didn't see them bones up close. It was Chick went close."

"Who's Chick?"

"This-yere boy. Chick Tuttle. I'm Lige Morse, but around yere we never use proper names. Chick saw some bones——"

"Bones? Heard in town it was a generally fair corpse."

Lige said, "Well, you know how talk gits twisted. I didn't say a whole dead corpse either. I just saw bones an' then left it to the Law."

The sheriff grumbled, hot as he was. "Hey, boy!"

I stuck my head up outa the Waller. Started to say "Much obliged," like Effie said was polite, but he shouted, "Hey, boy! What you find anyhow? Man's bones? Kinda a skeleton?"

"Dang if I know. Never saw a skeleton. But there was a bone——"

"Bone! Just one bone?"

"Yeh, a bone stickin' out the dirt. Looked like a bone. Might been a clod, but might been a bone. Mebbe shin-bone, long bone——"

"Hell-a-mile! Nearer I get to this killin', less it looks. Tell you what, Lige, I ain't goin' to drive in this heat three miles furder to look at some ol' calf bone that boy found."

"That's right." Lige was sure relieved. "Less said, soon-est mended. It was that Marlow disappearin' that started Chick off."

"Yeh," I said. "An Earl Staley so startled when I said mebbe Marlow was murdered. Looked guilty to me. Looked——"

"Looked—looked—to you! Where's this man Staley?"

"Off in Custer County figgerin' to get married——"

"And this Marlow—just gone back to Texas, I bet. Gid-dap!"

The sheriff grunted for Lige and Ellis to get out of his rig. They got out, and the sheriff touched a fly off his roan horse with that fine whip. The outfit ambled on west, and he was still grumbling like a feller plumb disgusted.

"Take him to midnight to get back to courthouse," said Lige. "Pretty hot drivin'. And Effie's flyin' around killin' two roosters and fixin' big chicken dinner fer the sheriff right now an' he too mad to go back to eat it."

"Don't ever invite no sheriffs to dinner!" Ellis yelled.

"Don't ever go talk to no sheriffs anywhere!" I said.

Lige went on ahead of us, and the prairie was hot. He hated to tell Effie the sheriff was so plumb mad he wouldn't stay for dinner after she'd invited him. Effie didn't have any clear idea why he came down in the first place. It took Lige an' Ellis and me, all three, explaining all afternoon, and when we were done Effie sat down against the soddy wall and laughed until she had to throw her apron over her ears to stop it.

Lige stood it awhile, and then he grunted, "Now, what's the big conniption about?"

"You three dang fools!" she cried. "Land, I could die!"

We all three went out to the horse trough to wash up to eat. Anyhow we had the sheriff's chicken dinner, and it was fine. Effie, all sweaty in the soddy, kept laughing. "So Earl killed Marion, an' Chick finds his bones, an' the sheriff he can't find nothin'. Lands, you menfolks all kill me next laughin'!"

"Ain't nothin' funny havin' sheriffs snoopin' around," I said. "Say, if anybody here's friend o' mine, don't tell Earl I swore he shot anybody. I just said—well, it wasn't a very big bone anyhow. Mebbe just a dry clod—mebbe just——"

"You boys git out to bed. I'm sore laughin' at you all."

Took me a long time to get asleep under the old wagon. Made me sore to get laughed at.

# 9

## Too Much Politics (East Road)

O NE day Effie said, "Someday we're goin' to have a flower garden like Gebauer's. The first thing Germans do is put in flowers when they have first-breakin' land. This summer it was prettier than ever because Miss Frawleen took care of it."

"Every time you go down there you come back an' tell us what ol' Worsenever is doin'. Cooks better 'n everybody. Knows about tendin' sick baby-kids. Now, flowers."

Effie was digging down under the Californy dress in her trunk. "Chick, it's a sign an' symptom."

"What's a sign o' what? Flowers is?"

Ellis said, "I know what Ma's meanderin' about in her mind. It's gettin' pore ol' Earl hooked up in marryin'. He better slope out."

Effie dug up an old blue chiny vase and said triumphantly, "Had this since I was a little girl. Might be hundred years old. It was weddin' present once to my mother. It's goin' to be weddin' present again for Miss Frawleen. I'm just startin on 'em early."

"Yeh, I guess. Neither of them galoots know it yet." I went out plumb disgusted. In the fall boys had lots to do. Besides the regular chores, milking, swilling the hogs, we rounded up all the chickens and turkeys—what was left of

131

them from the coyotes, polecats and hawks—after summering on the open prairie. Chickens had no coops at Lige's. They wintered in the straw cow barn or the frame horse stable, roosting on harness pegs, horses' backs, anywhere they could, making a mess for Ellis and me to clean up. Nobody knew how many chickens we had; they were never counted or cared for.

One day Lige hauled grain to town, and Effie was down at the German's helping make a quilt. She saved rags all the year around for quiltin' time. It was a rare thing when we had a whole day with nobody home but us. I promptly climbed the windmill ladder, which was strictly forbidden us. I could squirm under the big wheel above the platform and look away off all around.

Ellis would climb as far as the hole in the platform, but he thought he was too fat to lie out under the wheel. Anyhow he was a cautious boy, always waiting to see if I made it. I'd lie out flat under the big wooden blades and watch 'em come down almost on me. Ellis would yell, "You better scrooge yore belly lower. Draw in yore breath! If that wheel catches yore galluses or anything, you'll be whirled up an' around and throwed off an' hit the ground half killed dead."

Well, the blade tips never touched me. Cleared by an inch, then I'd suck some breath in. Ellis hung to the ladder top, advisin' me and glad when I'd crawl down. But from the platform you could see miles. Only thing that stuck up forty feet maybe. You could see the Rooshins' place, and Gebauer's two-story white house looked close. Other windmills very far off. Not many. Some first-breakin' farmers hadn't got windmills yet. Hauled their water from dug wells, but if you had much stock that was just mean work for boys.

"Git down off there afore you git killed!" Ellis would start slowly down the ladder.

I waited a little time. Hadn't had a chance to get up here for four months, the last time Effie went to town. "Don't pester me. Yore scared to git here on account o' bein' fat. Say, I see the whole world around me! Far as I see, it is round to the sky. Mebbe the Joggerfee's got it right."

"Get down. I'll tell Effie you was up the windmill."

But he wouldn't. We never told on each other, no matter what happened. If either busted anything on the place, it would just be a plumb mystery. Don't ever tell grownups anything. Effie grumbled finally that we were just liars, but that was all. Lige would grumble a little, then laugh and make excuses for us. He was kind of a boy, too, which was the reason he had such a time with the Mortgage every November. Scratching around to pay Intrust. Effie made him save for the durn thing, no matter what.

Well, this morning before I climbed down I yelled at Ellis. That Mortgage just put me in mind of Back East, so I gave a mean look that way. Then I hollered, "Say, I see two new windmills 'way off yander east. Wasn't there last spring. This country's growin'!"

"Well, if you'll get down afore you break yore neck, we'll start explorin' East Road like we intended a long time now."

"Yeh? All right. If so, I'll come down. But it's pretty up here. See something like trees 'way off east."

I came to the ground, and we hooked buttermilk out of the one cool mud spot under the tank pipe. I said, "You promised, now!"

"Sure. Tomorry we start. East Road's the last one to tackle. We travel a whole day, mebbe see something new. Won't be any hanged fellers anyhow. Effie says Back East they got Law an' Order."

"Well, I don't want to see any Law an' Order. That dang sheriff cooked me on Law an' Order, cussin' me like he did about Marlow's bones. I bet they *was* Marion's bones. Sheriff wouldn't even go look."

"Well, anyhow, Marion's gone somewhere, fancy clothes an' all. An' Earl ain't got back from Custer County, an' if he's tryin' to be a farmer on account of Effie eggin' him on, git married to Frawleen an' all, he's goin' to be licked. Earl hates to see prairie broke up fer corn."

"Me too. Well, we'll start Back East tomorry early."

Come daylight next morning it was mighty cold under the old covered wagon. We crawled out from the hay and horse blanket shivering. Pretty soon we'd have to sleep nights in the lean-to for the winter and wear boots and wade snow waist-deep to school. Ellis would try to catch up with other scholars in his class. I was all right for learnin', for I'd just whang away in the old Second Reader and Teacher'd see I was pretty smart, rattlin' off what was in it so quick. She'd think I was just starting the stuff.

Well, about day we got Jewel and Tops out the corral after we'd fed them big. I had on my new school wamus, and I stuck corn bread and fried pork inside it like we always did explorin' roads.

We were a long way toward Back East by sunup. Pretty

soon we saw cornfields and men husking. East Road was marked better than any others, but when we met a wagon outfit we rode out aside and lifted a hand. Didn't pull up and talk like grown folks would do seeing strangers. After a while we saw two houses away off. Then about noon it was all corn and stubble and we saw four houses. Ellis said, "It's like Effie claimed. Back East is lot o' people an' Law an' Order. Hey, I see a buggy comin'!"

"Pertend not to see the feller when we pass. Might be a sheriff."

Just a couple of girls. They yelled hello and were all dressed up. We didn't even grin. Better be suspicious of strangers this far Back East. This was a real traveled road now. Where it crossed another there were deep ruts. There must be a lot of folks living around here. After a couple of hours Ellis said he saw a railroad off north. But we kept on east. We'd seen a dang railroad before up North Road where we got the hanged man's rope. We stopped and ate and let the animals graze and drink under a road culvert and then rode on. Then we saw cottonwood trees growing each side of the road. And houses, some with two stories. Then we saw a lot of stores on a street, and at its end was a railroad station.

So many people made Ellis mighty anxious. When we saw a boy in short pants he looked so funny I started laughing. Ellis whispered, "Dry up! Liable to be a lot o' boys in store clothes, an' if they see us in wamuses Effie made they'll start to chase us outa their town. Keep outa sight, Chick."

Well, that was so. We sneaked around and tied the horses to a fence and crawled through the weeds to where we could see the railroad station where the crowd was thickest. Wagons and buggies all around full of folks too. Then I saw a big four-seat buggy with red, white and blue cloth tied all over it.

"What 'n tunket's goin' on?" Ellis whispered.

"Train's comin', that's it! Excitement just like we had when we saw a train. An' listen to that, will you?"

A train was crawling in to stop. People began to yell. Then I saw some big brass horns and drums like we'd seen in pictures. "Hey, that's a music band like they have Back East!"

It was getting dark now, and we felt safe, hidden in the big roadside weeds. The band neared, and we saw and heard everything.

The first music I ever heard in my life. The fellers made it so loud now that it was pretty scary till you got used to it. The crowd was thickest by one of the yellow cars. A big man came out and waved a shiny hat. I knew that was a real plug hat that Lige cussed about when he thought of the Mortgage. That feller must have come from 'way Back East—New York or some of them places. New York Mortgage man in a plug hat!

Ellis scrooged lower in the weeds and said, "What's he out here fer anyhow? Makin' all these folks so excited that they just stand there yellin'? If that feller came out to the ranch, I'd take a crack at him with the muskit. He feels too dang big if that's a plug hat."

"It is fer a fact. High an' shiny. Back East hat. Well, fer once Lige was tellin' truth. Say, that outfit's comin' this way."

The band was ahead of the two-horse rig, making a big

noise. Then men were coming along the carriage with kerosene cans on poles, it looked like, and when they lit these the street just dazzled us. We wanted to see it all, but this crowd was getting too close. Then two men came along around the corner and stopped near us.

One said, "Come on, Jake, an' hear the congressman. First one ever got out this far."

The other said, "I ain't goin' to join any procession an' go back on my idees about politics. I ain't goin' to vote fer any damn Republican."

"Come on an' hear what he talks about."

Jake wouldn't budge. "Let 'em yell. I'm not scared o' what he says. I'm a Democrat an' don't care who knows it."

The other man grumbled and went on to join the procession. Jake waited until the band wasn't a hundred feet away, and then he ducked back in the dark.

In the weeds Ellis punched me. "We better light out too. Lige says he's a Dimmycrat, so I must be a Dimmycrat. You live with us, so yore a Dimmycrat."

"I dunno. Never thought of it, I guess. This Dimmycrat has got back safe from 'em, so mebbe we better slope out too."

"Yeh. They're gettin' too close fer me."

The band let out a terrible shriek, and the torches waved. The carriage stopped in front of a store porch, and the man in the plug hat wiped his chin. Everybody yelled and got closer. I saw some of them boys in short pants racing around toward us, and maybe they'd want to fight, us just dressed up in farm wamuses and being Dimmycrats.

Ellis got up in the dark. "Git out o' here!"

I got up and ran after him back where we'd tied Ol'
Tops and Jewel. We got on them and lit out. Ellis said,
"I ain't scared, but that crowd's gittin' too excited fer me!"

"Yeh, if we got in a row, bein' Dimmycrats, we might
be stuck in jail. Anyhow I'm hungry, an' it's a long ways
to Lige's place."

"We got too far Back East, in politics an' all. I'm like
that man Jake—don't want to mix with Republicans."

We had certainly gone too far Back East. As usual when
we started to explore the roads around our corner, we went
so far that it took all night to get home, Ol' Tops not able
to do more than a fast walk. In the starlight silence we
corralled the horses and crawled into the hay under the
tattered covered wagon. When I woke up it was bright
day, but I had to wait until I could pull my eyes open and
wash them in the horse trough. In September I always got
"matterated" eyes, from some kind of weed seeds or dust,
Effie said, but there wasn't much to do about them except
wash them open. We went to breakfast in the soddy, and
Effie had saved coffee and everything for us.

She said, "I found you boys had been traipsin' off somewhere all yesterday and all night. What you find out this
time?"

"A feller with a plug hat an' a music band. Some big
town off East Road, I guess thirty mile mebbe. We lit
out fer home because we're Dimmycrats, ain't we?"

"You're just rapscallions, that's what. Git the wash boiler in an' on the stove. Fill it up an' git a paddle o' soap
from the barrel. You got to work today, if you are Dimmycrats. Lige is only Dimmycrat around here I know of. I
wouldn't go around braggin' of it if I was you."

# 10

## Who's Got a Fiddle?

AT LAST Effie said we'd have to go back to school, for we were just lazing around, pretending to work. She wouldn't even listen to my protest that I couldn't sit down on anything without that tar on my sores sticking fast and hurting so bad that even an Indian couldn't stand it. She inspected my bottom and said, "You git to school. You don't git educated at this end anyhow. Git on yore new wamus an' start. An' inquire around if anybody knows anybody that's got a fiddle."

I'd never heard a fiddle, but I knew what it was. On the way to school, while I was trying to limp so anybody could see how I suffered, Ellis said, "Fiddle be danged! That's another sign an' symptom. Fiddles is fer weddin's, so Effie's lookin' 'way ahead, an' somebody ought to go warn Earl Staley of what's goin' on unsight an' unseen with him in the middle of it."

"I tried to warn Earl twice an' he tells me to git to hell outa his business. Wish we had some way o' scarin' him good."

But Ellis and I forgot weddin's and fiddles, for now we were in for a bad week at the ranch. Once a year some distant relatives of Lige came in from their homestead 'way over east somewhere and then there wasn't peace any more.

139

They came in a wagon, a Civil War widda with four girls who were some sort of cousins, Effie said, Minnie, Mandy, Maggie and May—scrawny, barelegged shouting girls bigger than we were. Ellis and I lived in a panic while they were here. Their delight was to shove us around, off our feet, and kick, and if we got mad and started to fight it was worse. The only way to fight a girl is to grab her hair and try to yank her around. But this employed your hands, and theirs were free. They'd twist around and scratch your face. You had to let go of hair and run. And we didn't dare run to our secret fortress, the Buffalo Waller, for they'd follow us and likely tear things up. We just kept out of their way around the ranch and were glad when they and the widda hitched and departed. There were five girls at school but too little to fight.

So we didn't exactly say we were Dimmycrats when the big Webel boys said they were Republicans. Some days I had been used to wearing to school the little Johnny Reb cap which my father had left me when I was two years old, and telling some whoppers of how he got it off a general Down South, but this fall I left it hid at the Waller, what with politics an' all.

We all played Anty-High-Over with a ball made of a chunk of pewter, wrapped with string and then a piece of old denim tied around it. I'd never heard of baseball, football or any sport whatever, but the Webels had. Anty-High-Over consisted of splitting into two gangs, one on each side of the schoolhouse, and throwing the ball over the roof. The boy who caught it, if possible, dashed around the schoolhouse with his gang yelling. If he could hit anybody with that ball, the boy hit had to join his side. The old ball could hurt when the cover got loose. Anty-High-Over was never finished. We just played it until Teacher rang her bell. If any fight had developed, we'd all linger until she came out and interfered.

Fights had no rules, either. Punch, wrestle, kick, scratch, gouge, any way to get the best of it. Only don't kick a boy's leg sores if he had them. The idea in a fight was to bloody a nose. If you did that, you were winner. So every punch or kick was aimed at the nose if you got a boy down. Blood drew big yells from everybody, and then Teacher came out. So did Miss Frawleen Worsenever, but she didn't say a word—just watched, kind of disgusted. Like playing ball, fights had no rules.

We had that fine old word "honor." I don't hear it much these days. I don't know where the idea started among us. But if you had a big argument, a boy lying about something and you knew it, you'd say finally, "Now, on your honor! Say it on your honor if you dast."

That would make a boy stutter and get madder. He wouldn't say on his honor. To get out of that he'd likely aim a poke at your nose. No one wanted to say "on my honor" if he was lying. "Honor" started many a fight, trying to dodge saying it. So we were careful about using "honor" when we saw it made trouble.

Take the case of ghosts, now. Some boys believed in ghosts and were ready to fight for their idea, but no one would say on his honor he ever saw one. Ellis and I hooted at ghosts unless the other boy was too big. At home nobody believed in ghosts. Effie would laugh, and Lige say, well, back when he was a boy in Virginia, he'd heard—no, he never saw one, but he'd heard. But a dang ghost was no good. Just like wind, you could see right through ghosts, no insides, no nothin'. Ellis and I had no hope of ever finding one and so dismissed the idea.

Once Ellis asked me did I think that cowhand Marion Marlow, who'd vanished so suddenly, would make a good ghost. I still believed that, if we dug and hunted around that draw where we'd seen buzzards and started all that rookus with the sheriff, we'd find a dead man. The sheriff didn't know everything. Marion had been shot and buried, all right, but he didn't leave any dang ghost behind him to prove it. But I didn't talk about the case any more and get Law started up again.

Once Lige brought a letter from town which must have been there weeks waiting for him to haul wheat again. A letter made considerable excitement. Effie was the only one who ever got a letter. She could read it fine, she said. Lige couldn't, and Effie wouldn't let Ellis and me get our dirty paws in it. It was from Earl Staley, and he was coming back again. Seems that our place was the only thing like home this cowhand knew.

"Earl writes a better hand than any of you dumb critters. He's got his sod walls up, an' he's goin' clear up to Platte Bottoms to git poles fer a roof. Now if he only had some boards fer sheathin' the roof . . ."

She looked at Lige, and Lige was pained. "I ain't got a piece o' board on the place big enough fer a chicken roost. These boys grab every stick big enough fer any use and take it out to their dugout in the Waller."

"They don't need any boards. We can tear their roof off."

This started the worst roar from Ellis and me you ever

heard of. Ellis yelled, "No, you don't! We ain't stole any boards!"

"On your honor?"

Ellis began to stutter. "Well, j-just some little s-scrap pieces no good here."

I said, "Look here, it's on account o' gittin' married he wants a roof on his soddy. If you just would stop eggin' him on about gittin' married, he wouldn't need a roof. We ain't got any roof summertimes sleepin' under the wagon. Winters, Earl can come back an' sleep in a straw shack like he always done."

Lige said gloomily, "Yeh, woman, you stop this talk about it. If Earl gits married an' goes to Custer County, I won't have anybody to play seven-up with snowed-up nights."

"You bet!" I yelled. "Never heard of a married cowhand! Let him alone."

Ellis said, "Besides, this long-legs German girl never heard of it."

"Miss Frawleen got more education than anyone around here in miles," Effie said. "She's been a nurse too in Old Country."

"Yeh, all in Dutch. Ol' Rooshin Toby he talk better 'n Miss Worsenever. I told him how to cuss in English."

Lige said, "Effie, you stop messin' in. Earl ain't no good farmin', but he's a dang good cowhand. You're goin' to ruin a good hand tryin' to make him settle down on a piece o' land."

Effie went behind her sheeting wall and pulled out her trunk. She sang out cheerfully, "Love will find a way!"

Then she put Earl's letter in with her book and came

back to the oilclothed table with the lamp on it and said, "Any o' you boys had your dirty paws in my trunk?"

"No, ain't nothin' there we want except a swig o' Pain Killer. You let me suffer all summer with sores an' cuts an' tar on 'em an' wouldn't give me any Pain Killer."

"An' start you growin' up a whisky-head! Pain Killer's fer bellyache an' Good fer Consumption, it says on the bottle. You all go to bed an' lemme alone. I want to read some more in the book."

Lige went to hauling off his boots behind the sheet wall. Ellis and I went out and crawled into the blankets and hay under the wagon. Getting cool these nights. First real cold snap, we'd have to sleep in the lean-to. But if we slept there, there'd be sheets on the bed. Effie wouldn't let us sleep on sheets unless we washed our feet, and we wouldn't think of that until time to get into school boots for winter.

Lige was hauling wheat this month, having the Mortgage in mind for November. School went on pretty good. Ellis and I lit out for the Buffalo Waller every afternoon when we were out. The other boys from over south headed for home at once. No one ever bothered trailing us to the Waller. We were pretty busy in the dugout under the rim of sod. There was one job that a boy could work at in spare moments and never complete. That was getting the rusted ramrod out of the old Kentucky long rifle. We dug down the muzzle with bits of wire, hoping to twist it. We dribbled precious powder into the breech vent grain by grain and touched a match, hoping to blow the rod out. The powder blew back in our faces. We tackled this project every summer, but it never was any good.

Then we turned to molding bullets for the muskit from a few scraps of lead and pewter hooked from Lige's workbox. This bullet mold was another rusty relic. We had a time melting the lead on a small iron kettle over a fire, and that was a problem. Grass wouldn't do. We roamed the ranch to hook scraps of boards from the horse stable, the cottonwood poles from fences. Lige would discover it later, but too late. Out in the Waller we got some lead melted and poured it into the mold. The mold was full of rain water, and the lead spattered back on our faces. That hurt. Then we had lead spangles on our cheeks and hair. We had to confess; and Lige and Effie had to pick the lead out of our skins. The burns swelled up, but now we had a reason for not going back to school. Lige said if I'd read the big Dick-dick book I'd know better. Effie said, "Well, mebbe that book is too big fer Chick. Lige, you better look around fer some book he can carry easy."

"Like hell! There ain't no such critter in this country. I ain't goin' to pester the boys in Jake's place about it ag'in." Lige looked dang miserable.

I said, "Look, now we got four books—three in the trunk and one at the Waller. We don't need more books."

Thinking how stuff from Effie's trunk smelled made me remember how Marion Marlow's buckaroo outfit had smelled of camphor. Out at the Waller, where we were always digging the dugout bigger, Ellis and I talked about that mystery all the time. With winter ahead we couldn't explore the country any more, but, we'd been on all the four roads leading from Lige's corner, the center of America sure—if you looked at the map right—and they were all mighty interesting. Except the Indians. They were a disappointment: just hungry and didn't try to scalp us. Election time came, but Lige wouldn't go to town and vote. Now he said he wasn't a Dimmycrat but wanted to join a new party. A man in town told him there would be a party someday agin the Railroad and monopoly. Ellis asked Teacher when there would be a new party like that, and that girl got excited. She was against it, she said; just a lot of wild talk, and it would wreck the country. Well, we didn't care; that would be some excitement. If Lige would hitch and go, we'd all start to help wreck the country. But Thanksgiving was coming, and we forgot the country.

One Sunday Teacher and Miss Worsenever drove up in Gebauer's buggy. Ellis and me got behind the corral, for we hated company coming. In a minute those three women were all jawing about me. Sin and a shame, Teacher said, I didn't have a new Reader. Miss Frawleen pitched in with Dutch talk; Effie denounced Lige and the two saloonkeepers.

Ellis and I were getting set to depart for the Waller when he yelled, "Look! Earl Staley ridin' in on West Road!"

"Sure is. I knew he'd show up afore Thanksgiving dinner."

Earl jogged in to the soddy, leading his two scrawny pack animals as always. Not a critter had got an ounce of fat on him out in Custer County. Earl either. The big lummix was all dusty and peaked and hungry-looking. He didn't see us, but when the three women came hollering out the door he grinned and slung a leg off and shook hands.

Effie ran to get him water and some cookies. Teacher,

who was just curious about cowhands, went to fingering Earl's Winchester sheath and rope and all the stuff hung on his saddle. Earl stood laughing a little, Miss Frawieen smiling and chewing off what words she knew.

Ellis and I sneaked around the windbreak and took off for the Waller. We had to consider something. We'd got the sheriff out here on account of saying we found Marion Marlow's bones and who'd killed him except Earl anyhow, them two hands fighting over a girl?

"He'll be sore when he hears what you said. I didn't talk any."

"Well, I sure saw some bones. An' Earl just looked funny when anybody asked where'd Marion go all of a sudden. Earl wouldn't answer."

"Well, watch what you say. Don't start no trouble."

"Earl don't want no trouble; just wants a square meal. I bet he ain't farmin', ain't got a work team, ain't got a plow, ain't got nothin'. He don't want to git hooked with any woman either, I bet."

"Then he better slope out o' here. Effie says she never heard of a weddin' in this country, ten years now, an' she's after Earl good an' heavy. Well, I ain't goin' to have hand in it."

For once I didn't answer Ellis in an argument.

Earl stayed with us, fooling around with some range critters still off somewhere westward, looking for calves and yearlings that might be Lige's, and anyhow he said he could rope and brand 'em, even if Lige didn't want them. Just wanted to act like he was useful and also dodge any farmwork. Effie made him one of the family, mended his clothes and washed them, made dried-apple pie the

way he liked; for a fact, I saw she was just leading the
pore feller on. She was mighty cheerful, having a new
interest in life. Once she asked me, "Is it so the Webels
over south got an organ?  Ask 'em at school."

"Yeh, I heard.  Webel boys kind of pick on me, so I
don't fool with 'em.  But the Rooshins up North Road,
they got a fiddle.  I seen it once when I rode lead horse
for Toby harvestin'."

"Land, a fiddle!  That's better!  Never heard any music
in all the ten years since we settled here.  You boys are
sure raised just heathen.  Never heard any music in yore
lives."

"Heard that band which played fer politics when we
was off East Road.  What you want music fer?  Ain't we
got trouble enough now?"

She laughed and looked off to the edge of prairie, brown
and frosted now with a cold snap. "I'm just plannin'.  You
boys need boots pretty soon.  But a fiddle's more important
right now.  You know them Rooshins better 'n anybody.
Find out who plays the fiddle."

Lige came in and heard.  Out in the corral when he unhitched he said, "What's that woman eggin' you on to
do?"

"Oh, I know!  It's on account of Earl.  She says at weddin's they always have a fiddle."

"Back in West Virginny we always had a mountain man
to fiddle at weddin's.  But, hell, Earl's no hand to git married!"

"She set her mind now on a fiddle."

"When that woman sets her mind on a thing you better

git out her way." Lige grinned. "That's the way she got me an' started fer Californy. Busted down now, but she'll git there yet."

"Yeh, but this is different. This German lady don't know that we're all tryin' to git her married. Nobody's asked her yet; Earl ain't got sand enough to go shine up to her."

"Well, then," said Ellis, "Chick's got to ask her. He always gits messed up in trouble of some kind."

"Hell I'll ask her! I can't talk Dutch, an' anyhow she ain't willin' to forgive an' forget about the windmill tank."

Lige scratched his ear. "Boys, it's a problem. But mebbe I can find a fiddle. That feller at Jake's that got you the readin' book so big you can't lug it, he knows a hand who plays fiddle. I ain't heard music since I come Out West."

Effie had come to the door and listened. "Listen—I don't want no whisky-soaked fiddle fer the weddin'. We got to go to town soon to get the boys winter boots. An' you got to pay Intrust on the Mortgage."

Lige looked dubious. He'd forgotten all about the Mortgage. Effie went on: "An' you got to look around fer a Reader fer Chick. Nobody around this place able to make head or tail outa that dictionary. Got to find Chick a Reader."

Lige scratched his other ear, looking more doubtful. He'd forgotten all about Third Reader also. "Well, I'll ask in Jake's place ag'in. Somebody must know about them dang Readers."

"Chick don't want any whisky-soaked Reader. Land

only knows what you'll bring back next, tryin' to get that boy educated, an' I promised his father afore he died that I'd see he was brung up proper."

"This ain't no place to grow up proper. We better all hitch an' start to Californy ag'in."

One cold November day we all started to town with a load of wheat. A frosty ride, with Lige and Effie in the front spring seat and Ellis and me sitting on the grain with our legs buried to the knees to keep them warmer. As usual we all had to yell at the five dogs to keep them from chasing after the wagon. Getting started to town was an uproar you could hear clear to Mr. Gebauer's. When the sun came up we were far past the Rooshins' white-plastered house with the smoke from the chimney. They had coal even this early, while Lige had to wait on the Mortgage before he could get even a little load that might last past Christmas. After that, snowed in, we'd burn cobs, corn, hay in the cookstove. But Effie would sing even as she scolded us, vowing she'd tan our hides someday. But in all the years I never knew her to lay a hand on any boy, or cat or dog or any creature. They were all pore dumb critters; and when she knew cattle were dying in the winter drifts her little songs would die also and she'd stare out the soddy window and wish all the world was fed and sheltered as we were.

But this frosty day to town all the world sparkled. Lige whacked his team to a trot. The load of wheat rumbled and jolted. Ellis and I shivered in the new wamuses dismally. We hated town and all civilizations: boots, sheriffs, schools and books. All except the Joggerfee book with the maps which showed how we were in the Center of America with the four roads leading on to Mystery from our section corner. Now this North Road to town was mighty cold, so it ended up with boots. I thought of South Road, the pleasant river of the plum trees. If a man traveled far enough south, he wouldn't need boots. But Rebels might shoot at him. Effie told me that my father had been a Colonel in the Yankee Army, and sometimes she'd take his picture out of her trunk and let me see it— if I'd wash my dirty paws.

# 11

# A Bath for Thanksgiving

COLDER days came, with boots and starting to school again. Thanksgiving was near, so Ellis and I had to take a bath. Effie was stubborn in some ways about housekeeping. Summer days sometimes we crawled into the water tank, but Lige wouldn't let us use soap there, for the stock didn't like it. Dang if I blame cows for that. When we crawled out we had green stuff and maybe wiggle-tails in our hair, and all for nothing. Nobody knew that wiggle-tails turned into mosquitoes.

A winter bath was more excitement. Effie put the wash boiler on the stove, and Ellis built a good fire. I dragged the wooden washtub out on the hard dirt floor. We couldn't start any fool bath until grown-up folks went to bed behind the cotton-sheet wall. Then they yelled advice how to have a bath.

Ellis and I stripped by the stove. At this end of the soddy, besides the stove, were the oilclothed table with the lamp, four chairs and a couple of shelves where they kept pots and pans and dishes, stuff like that. We always swore there wasn't room in the house for a bath, but Effie kept nagging. Then when we got to yelling good and splashing water at each other she'd shout that we'd knock all the dishes down, and Lige'd yell that we were getting his tobacco wet and the lamp would get upset and the house catch fire and general conniption go on if we fooled around with a durn bath. We took turns in the washtub and ladled on soft soap and maybe Effie's bar of hard soap, and shoved and howled, the whole place full of suds. Then we had to scrape soap off each other. It was pretty exciting.

The yelling would start all the dogs to barking outside. Then Lige would yell again through the sheet wall that he couldn't sleep and would be all worn out for work the next day if we didn't quit before nine o'clock. Well, we soaped and rubbed with towels or sacking and lugged the tub out to empty on the frosty grass and then ran to get under the blankets on the hay under the wagon. I always felt pretty scratchy after a bath, skin all puckered up. We left the dirt floor in the soddy muddy, and Effie said she had to clean house all over again.

This time we complained that it was pretty early for a bath; but Effie said, "Well, you got to clean up. I heard there was a preacher ridin' circuits over south, an' he might come through here. An' I certainly would like to have a preacher around sometime."

Then she looked mysterious again, and I knew what she meant. Earl Staley would be with us for Thanksgiving, and Miss Frawleen could talk pretty good English now, and Effie was bound to hook them up.

Lige said, "Yeh, preacher around. That means big chicken dinners fer Sundays, an' you boys got to be polite. You got to say 'Much obliged' an' stop cussin' the cows an' all."

"Don't want any preacher around. Scare you worse 'n sheriffs. Makes me feel hostile worse 'n Indians."

"Listen to 'em," said Effie. "Growin' up like just heathen."

Didn't fool me. She sent word by us to school for Miss Frawleen to come visit us again. Ol' Worsenever had been pretty busy all summer, we heard, going around to see if anyone was sick.

Effie said lots of people knew her now because she went around telling them how to raise baby-kids, stuff like that. She'd been a nurse in the Old Country and was mighty useful. Not for Ellis and me; we lit out for the Waller if we saw Gebauer's buggy drive up. Worsenever found a wagon outfit down on the crick, everybody sick with malaria, and took them to Gebauer's and doctored them until they could pull west again. They stopped at our place and said how good ol' Worsenever was. Lige gave them half a hog and three sacks of flour and a lot of potatoes; and they pulled out for Custer County where, maybe, they could take a homestead before cold weather.

There were three children and a woman in this wagon outfit besides the man, who'd been in Sherman's army in Georgia. When Effie heard that, she got out my father's picture from the trunk and asked if the veteran had ever met him.

"Well, no, hardly," the man said. "He was a Colonel, I see by his shoulder straps, an' I was just Tennessee boy an' didn't know officers. But I admire fer to see this Colonel."

So I got to see my father's picture again. Effie kept it wrapped up in her trunk, as she did her Bible, so we wouldn't get paws on it. The picture was certainly grand in a gold frame; he had big black whiskers and a sword, and tassels on his hat. I'd been scared to even shake hands with a man grand as that, even if I had on a new wamus. Sometimes Effie got a few old letters he'd written her before I was born, and read them to us. About Vicksburg, and when he was wounded at the Battle of Allatoona. He lived long enough to get married after the war was over a few years. Then Lige would jibe in, so I heard a lot of talk about that war and so many of my folks in it—all restless folks, Effie said, never settle down long, always talking about Western Country and diggin' gold but never much good at farming. Cheerful folks, always laughing, she said. But doggone, that was Effie herself! She kept the whole ranch cheerful.

But that picture of the Colonel got me into trouble at school sometimes when I got to bragging big, like saying that it was my father who licked the whole Rebel Army and anybody with sense would know it. Sometimes it started a fight. I kept the little gray Rebel cap he'd left me hid out at the Waller, for it would start arguments too with the Webel boys who were bigger than I was. So Effie kept the picture wrapped and clean to give me when I grew up, able to fight.

Well, after the excitement, a bath and all, and the wagonman hitched and gone, fall work about done, the place was quiet.

One frosty dawn I had been out at the four roads' crossing, alone, just to see if the Middle of America was still there undisturbed by a wagon outfit that had passed yesterday. I searched in the grass for the iron stake. A last star was fading in the vast light, and suddenly I saw it again—in a puddle by my bare foot. A star in a cow track! I knelt down and stared. Mystery again! I looked at the dawn and then down again. My star was fading, and when I put a finger to the filmy water it was gone. I went back to breakfast with the folks in the soddy, but I was thinking, How queer—a star in a cow track! Earl was working the coffee grinder, Lige mending a bridle on the oilclothed table. Ellis had the other end spread with rooster feathers, trying to construct a Pawnee headdress.

Effie came from the plank cupboard, jerked the oilcloth, dumping all the stuff on the floor. She always had a time keeping her only table cleared for meals. She rattled plates and cups and pushed me back from the stove where I was trying to warm fingers. Then we all had breakfast—big hot buckwheats with grease gravy mixed with thick molasses, fried pork, fried eggs and all the coffee anybody wanted.

Big thick chunks of bread. What wonderful bread! In those days wheat bread tasted like wheat, corn bread tasted like corn. Buckwheat cakes were all buckwheat. No food was ever bleached, doctored up, enriched in any factory as it is today. The only breakfast food was plain boiled wheat; nothing ever came out of a package. Sugar was a fine dark brown, and you crumbled it from a keg. We had milk, but Ellis and I wouldn't touch it. It tasted of sage because in drought the cows ate the stuff. Ellis and I hated milk anyhow because twice a day we had to battle the half-wild cows to get any. Get a rope on them, drag them to a lariat pin, nose to the ground, and then watch out you didn't get kicked across the corral.

Our cows weren't so tough as range animals, but they

weren't tame either. If they kicked us and upset the milk pail, we could kick back, but a barefoot boy can ruin his feet kicking an ol' muley in the ribs. We'd bring a bucket of milk to the soddy for Effie to strain, get the hairs and dirt out of it and then put in flat pans for cream to rise. When she had enough cream she'd put it in the wooden churn, and then Ellis and I had to slam the dasher up and down maybe an hour to get butter. We didn't want it, but there was always so much butter that we greased old harness straps with it out at the Waller.

Cool weather coming on, we dug out under the side of the Waller to make the cave bigger and propped the roof with poles we swiped from Lige's horse shed. He always complained why his roof wouldn't hold up, just as Effie complained why her clothesbasket fell to pieces suddenly when she was washing. She didn't know that Ellis and I had discovered that the rattan was pretty good stuff to smoke, even if it did make your mouth mighty sore. You could pull smoke through the rattan pieces and strangle.

We cut so much away from the bottom that the basket fell apart and we had to quit smoking for a while. But she never laid it on us. Lige didn't find out either; he said it was the dang monopolists who swindled pore Western folks with shoddy stuff and he wouldn't vote any more until something was done about it.

Looking back now after some seventy years, I wonder what occupied our minds the long days and years. They didn't seem to lack any more than our hands, which were always busied.

There was the bright open land; there was the life, hard and cheerful. No Matthew Arnold sweetness and light, no gracious living, no perfectionism. No pretense, propaganda, glamour—advertising to sell cars or soap or whatnot with wondrous legs and dentures as the magazines do now. We never saw a magazine. Outside of our few miles under the great light nothing came to tell us of the world of affairs. Ours was a small hard world under the open sky. No hidden places for vice or intrigues. No robberies, plots of murder to fascinate boys as in the comics. What a life! There were the four roads luring us on to the unknown, but after a while we had no great curiosity about what lay beyond. We'd explored some twenty, thirty miles each way from the Center of America, and that was a mighty long way for a boy to go from Lige's ranch. Effie asked me one time what I intended to do when I grew up. I was rather astounded; I'd never given it a thought, and now a whole summer was past since I'd tried to bite the pup's tail off, so I must be growing up as he did.

If anybody loved me, I didn't know it. We never mentioned that word; it would be awful indelicate, like the four Pawnee words that I learned and which I mustn't say except at school. Love? That was something Effie got out of her storybook, and it certainly was going to make trouble. Only Effie ever said that word—love.

Marion Marlow came loping in one day from South Road, and his little roan looked pretty dusty and ganted up as if they'd traveled fast and a far way. He yelled, "Hey, Chick! How's the folks?"

Well, it made me stutter. I didn't know what to say. Here I'd claimed that he was dead and I'd seen his bones after Earl had shot and buried him. But I shook hands and said, "F-folks is all right. You been gone s-some time. Been to Texas?"

That made Marion kind of stutter too. "Oh, s-sure! Been ridin' with an old outfit Earl an' me was with long time ago. Had s-supper yet?"

"No, you go to the house an' see Effie. She's settin' bread."

Then Effie saw him and came out with her hands all flour and she grabbed Marion's like she was glad to see him. It surprised me when I'd thought she'd been trying to have him for a villain.

"Marion, yore a sight fer sore eyes. Come in an' eat. You look kinda peaked." He went to the soddy with her, and I thought she sniffed of his Mexican jacket with the big buttons and beads. He hung his big hat on the peg in the outside sod wall, and after a while I went and smelled it. It certainly smelled of something funny, but it wasn't camphor like in Effie's trunk.

That hat didn't look as if it had been worn a bit since Marion had jumped out of this neighborhood so suddenly. And he didn't look all sun-browned up like a rider would from some Texas roundup. Little pale and thin, I thought. That cowhand was lying about where he'd been.

I went in. Effie was feeding him yeast biscuits and molasses until she got supper, and he seemed certainly hungry. I passed his chair and smelled of his jacket. Same stuff. And his jacket wasn't dirtied up like a rider's would be. Effie saw me smelling of Marion's back and gave me a funny look. So I went and sat down, considering. Marion talked fast, kind of excited, so nobody could ask him ques-

tions. Before when he came up here he gave Effie some little fool thing like a china dog which she might think was
pretty. In September Marion had been rolling in money,
devilin' around the neighborhood, giving nickels to boys
and buying drinks in town. Now I heard him begin laughing kind of foolishly, and he said, "Well, the fact is I'm
broke. Goin' to hole up at my cousins' beyond Plum Creek
and help feed stock this winter."

"Well, that's too bad. A boy ridin' fer some cow outfit
all summer an' busted afore Christmas!"

"Yeh. Just little poker game down in Abilene. Cleaned
me."

Somehow I didn't believe him. That cowhand was
changed considerable. Wasn't nearly so brash as he used
to be with women.

Lige and Ellis came in from the North Eighty, where
they'd been husking. Then Earl rode in from trying to cut
out a few of Lige's cows from a little spread that was being
rounded up 'way off west of us to drive south before freeze
up. Marion ran out with a whoop and a holler to shake
with Earl. Earl didn't seem so surprised to see him, but
they grinned and talked kind of low so the rest of us
couldn't make it out.

Effie saw me smelling of the Mexican hat again. She
whispered, "Now you stop that! Ain't none o' yore business."

"Don't smell like it did before, like stuff you put on yore
Californy dress fer bugs."

"No, it don't. I don't know what this is now. But you
keep yore trap shut about these two boys—you made

enough rookus, the sheriff an' all, sayin' you found some ol' bones."

"Well, this is plumb mystery ag'in. Something's happened to Marion. He used to be a reg'lar case, whoopin' an' hollerin', shootin' a gun an' spendin' money, an' now he's come back to us ganted up like he didn't eat well. An' chuck wagons feed hands pretty good too."

"Chick, you keep still an' let me investigate this."

I tried to keep out of this grownups' business all I could, but once I just had to remark to Earl: "Yore friend Marion looks kinda played out an' busted, an' chuck wagons don't smell like that either, fer a fact."

Earl he just looked wooden-faced at me and said nothing. He rode off south with Marion to see if Marion's cousins 'way beyond Plum Creek could put him in their bunkhouse for winter. He was always looking after that rapscallion as if he was a young brother. Now Marion was broke, and Earl not much better off, and Effie trying to head him into a weddin'. I felt kind of sorry for those two cowpokes—cow business gone up in our country, and they wanted a place to winter comfortable. Well, it wasn't my business if Effie would let me stay out of it.

We all went to town again for mail and holiday stuff. Effie went all around the dozen houses or so, trying to find if she could get me a Reader. Lige didn't find any either at the two saloons, and now he was plumb disgusted with education. Effie bought wool to knit us socks and maybe a shirt apiece when big snows came. Effie never bought a thing for herself, but then she had the Californy dress saved up. Back at the ranch Effie cut our hair with the big

shears she used for pants. So we went back to school kind
of spruced up and didn't like it.

We never saw an overcoat. As weather grew colder
we got into more old woolen shirts and tied mufflers
around them and did pretty well, stuffed like that when
we worked. Miss Worsenever was in school, but she was
frosty to me, remembering how she got dumped in the
tank. Wouldn't forgive and forget, just like that Stealer
dog about his tail. I didn't care what either of them thought
of me. When school let out Ellis and I always headed for
the Buffalo Waller, for now we were afraid Effie would
steal some roof boards off it to give Earl for his new soddy
out in Custer County. We'd hooked them from Lige in
the first place. Then we didn't like what Effie had said
about kidnaping a girl like in her book and maybe hiding
her out at the Waller.

Ellis said, "I guess nobody will. Earl's too bashful an'
Marion's busted. An' he ain't a heller no more in buckaroo
clothes. Now I figger he wouldn't dast wear them kind
o' togs around a real cow outfit. He's had 'em packed in
a trunk, keeps 'em just to wear around us farm folks.
That's why they smelled o' camphor."

"They don't now. It's somethin' else, an' Effie is just
puzzled. She's never goin' to get them boys to fight over
any girl. Miss Frawleen don't know a thing about gittin'
married either. But I sure would like to hear them
Rooshins fiddle."

"Yeh, but it ain't worth a weddin' to hear a fiddle. Too
much excitement already around here, Chick, fer me."

So we went back to the ranch and did chores in the dark,

for there wasn't any kerosene left for the lantern. Lige was always forgetting something when he was in town.

It was getting pretty cold to sleep outdoors under the wagon, but when we thought of having to wash feet to sleep in the lean-to with sheets, we stuck it out. Feet kept clean anyhow, running summerlong in dew-wet grass, and dust didn't stick long except in your ears. Work was being laid by. Corncrib full with a big pile outside unshucked, and, as usual, there was no place to put it. The little granary leaked wheat all around, with another big pile next to it. Buckwheat we tried to keep sacked, for Lige said it would be bad for stock and his rusty wire fence wouldn't keep cattle from all this feed. We didn't worry: a lot would die in the blizzards before spring. Ellis and I cleaned out the pits again and stowed cabbage, potatoes, turnips and beets. Shoveled dirt on them and waited for snow to cover from freezing. Most would anyhow. Nobody seemed to care. All Lige would care for was his work stock; and Ol' Tops, the bony relic of the Californy adventure, got the warmest place in the stable. Snow would sift all through it anyhow. I cared for Tops most, for he was my riding animal even if he was too stiff to get off a walk. The five dogs fared best of all. They camped in the straw cow stable, the warmest spot on the ranch. But summerlong they piled in with us under the covered wagon.

The Dictionary was stowed in the dugout in the Buffalo Waller, and it would be snowed in good and tight until spring. Nobody said any more about it. I'd started in on the first page, which began with A and was easy, and then I'd got all tangled up and quit learning. Effie still fussed about Readers, but nobody else did any more. Lige would haul grain to town and come back very late in the dark singing:

"Settin' on the fence, didn't mean no harm,
When along comes a man, says, 'I'll buy yore farm.
I'll buy yore pigs an' yore corn so bloomin'—
But dang if I swap fer yore pore ol' woman!' "

The dogs all barked. Effie would wake up and light the lamp. I'd hear her say, "That fool has had a drink, an' I bet he never asked anybody ag'in about a Reader." Then she'd get up and warm supper for him. I'd go to sleep, safe again from more learning.

One cold night Ellis punched me awake and yelled. He squirmed around and grabbed his neck. I put my hand out and felt a dog's leg. Then a wet pup. Then another wet pup. We both crawled out and dragged the blanket. Rachel, the blue bitch, snugged down in the warm spot, looking pleased.

Ellis yelled, "Dang her, had pups right against my ear! Five already!"

"Well, hell, we can sleep in the cow barn! Cool night like this, let pups have the blankets."

But Ellis was mad. He said, "Now if Effie hears this I'll have to take another bath, an' I ain't through scratchin' from the last one." But we went to the barn and dug in the straw where the milk cows couldn't step on us.

Next morning we counted seven pups. We got an old box, filled it with straw and snugged it alongside the barn.

But the next night Rachel lugged them all back and piled them between us and curled up on Ellis' stomach. We had a time breaking her of that trick. Ellis washed his ears and didn't tell Effie the truth about it. Lige said it was funny, that boy washing his ears again. Maybe some preacher was coming. We had never seen one yet. Lige said it was no way to bring up boys, who never had seen a funeral or a weddin' yet. I thought a funeral would be better—maybe not so much fuss as Effie was planning for this weddin' of Earl and Frawleen, and they didn't even know it.

Ellis said I ought to go warn Miss Frawleen, for now she was learning a lot of English and did big sums on the blackboard at school that sometimes seemed to knock even Teacher flat. It was no use warning Earl—he'd tell me to git th' hell out o' his business. Lige told me not to take any stock in what Effie planned; it was all some foolishment and made her sing and giggle. But I began to consider these grownups more than I had. They didn't seem so old as they had at first. I guess Effie and Lige weren't fifty yet, and Earl maybe thirty. Frawleen was young as Teacher, maybe, and always spruced up.

These two cowhands, living up here for the winter, were invited to Mr. Gebauer's for supper, and Marion said Frawleen was a dang fine cook. Old wooden-faced Earl just didn't say anything. But he offered us a dime for a pup to give Miss Frawleen when they were big enough. Effie said not to take any money; that pore feller couldn't afford a dime. He had to save money to get married on, but he didn't even know that yet.

So we now had twelve dogs, little and big, and Effie wouldn't hear of drowning pups as some people did. But

she saw that they all ate hearty, always cooking enough
for the whole outfit as well as nine cats, so they all hung
around the door, waiting for her, and sometimes the big
dogs would knock Effie down in the snow and trample her
and she'd laugh.

Ellis and I had no particular dog friends among them as
you read in storybooks. They weren't that kind of dogs
like in stories. There was one lesson in a Reader about a
dog that loved a boy and jumped in a river and saved his
life. Well, I couldn't figure our dang dogs would do anything of the kind. It was just another fool story as books
had.

But then our dogs didn't have a river to jump into to save
anybody. Anyhow they'd never think of it. After I read
that story of how the dog loved the boy and the boy loved
his dog I wondered why Old Bluch and Tige and Fido, the
biggest dogs, didn't offer help that time I got all tangled up
with the bobbed wire. I was helpless till Earl hauled me
loose. All the dogs did was sit around and scratch fleas and
grin. When I fell off the windmill frame and couldn't
walk on account of my back Tige came up and smelled
of my ear. Bluch wouldn't do a thing except scratch
fleas. Our dogs were always looking out for themselves,
an' to heck with you! Try to have 'em chase a cow out of
the garden an' they'd chase the wrong cow. Sick 'em on a
pig and they'd grab the pig's ear so he couldn't get out of
the cabbage patch as you wanted. Well, at school I read
a lot of stuff about dogs and boys too which didn't make
much sense. Earl told Lige that the trouble was that our
dogs growed up plumb heathen just like us with no train-
ing. Back in Arkansaw where he was a boy he used to get

whaled into some sense. Lige'd just laugh. He never whaled anybody, not even a mule.

Effie didn't either. Jawed some, but mostly laughed and sang and read in her storybook how to fall in love and have a lot of trouble but all was happy at the end of it. I guess that story kept her going, little skinny woman, about ninety pounds, and all the work in house and out that she did. Like the time when Marion came loping home from town with a big can of ice cream because Ellis and I had never seen any. The can fell over in the soddy, and it was full of warm soupy stuff that we didn't like, but all the flies in the county piled in on us, buzzin' in the ice-cream mud on the floor. Marion was sure broke up—and Effie laughed while she tried to clean the mess.

She had so much ice-cream mud to clean up that finally Lige invited in all the cats and dogs to help by licking the stuff. Marion went out to sit on the corral poles and felt mean. "Look here, boys, I'll sure git you ice cream one o' these days. Or I'll make it. Earl an' me'll rush a block of ice home sometime an' I'll stir up a kettle an' freeze it."

"Sure," I said. "Make it fer the weddin'?"

"Weddin'? What weddin'?"

I started to talk, but Ellis yelled, "Aw, shut up! It's a surprise! Effie's fixin' it up, but nobody knows."

"Yeh? If people don't know they're goin' to be married, how'n hell can you fix it?"

"Dang if I know. I ain't meddlin'."

Marion sat there, staring at his cow horse as if ideas were too much for him. I thought I better throw him off the track so he wouldn't meddle. So I said, "Aw, mebbe it's a funeral. Effie's set for some big doin's."

Lige came out, kicking dogs away. The dogs sat down, licking ice-cream mud off each other. Effie'd lit the lamp to finish cleaning up, and she was singing.

Marion said, "What's this I hear? Weddin's? If there was another beat-all woman around like Effie, I reckon menfolks would want to git married. She's a caution, that woman."

Lige sat on the fence. "Oughta seen her when we started fer Californy. Year afore the Railroad came in. Got a fine new dress fer Californy, an' singin' too. Then, crossin' this prairie, headed west, the off critter took heaves an' died right where this corral stands now. Well, we couldn't travel with just Tops on the wagon. Spring come, prairie looked so pretty she said 'Let's stay here an' take up land.'

"So we did, by golly! Got another horse for first-breakin' sod. Then built the soddy an' proved up the homestead. Then Ellis was born in the soddy. Then Chick's father died somewhere down in Mexico, him dang near a General then, but he didn't leave Chick nothin' but a ol' Johnny Reb cap an' the muskit. So Chick come live with us, Effie still singin'. But never got her Californy dress outa her trunk ner her Bible. She got camphor fer the trunk to keep her stuff from bugs an' moths. Twelve years now. Now, Chick, you ride Ol' Tops around ex-plorin' roads, an' him so stiff he can just walk, but you oughta seen Young Tops on his way to Californy! Him an' Effie, young-like. Why, right today, some fine mornin's I see Ol' Tops cockin' his ears over west'ard. He ain't fergot Californy-bound. I wanted to start ag'in west'ard when I got another wagon horse, but Effie said we'd have to wait because ol' gray bitch of a dog we had had nine pups. Time Effie got 'em raised, too late in season to start fer Californy. I kept on breakin' prairie land."

"Yeh," said Marion. "Feller ought to settle sometime!"

"That's it!" I yelled. "Git married an' settle down! Why don't you?"

Marion looked kind of startled like Earl had done.

Ellis got in his say: "Yeh, or a funeral. We never saw either a weddin' or a funeral, growin' up plumb ignorant!"

"Hell-a-mile!" Marion said. "I seen funerals. They ain't much excitement. Now, a weddin', everybody could get drunk."

"An' I know where we can borry a fiddle!"

"Say," said Marion, "what's goin' on around here while I was gone?"

"You'll find out!"

Lige said, "You boys shut yore traps. Just somethin' outa a book."

I saw the lamp in the soddy door. Effie was singing.

Earl Staley came loafing over to sit with us menfolks. Lige said to Marion, "How you fixed fer Thanksgivin' dinner?"

"Well, I can eat with them cousins I got over south beyond the crick where I bed down. But they got a whole lot o' baby-kids an' they pile all over me if I sit down."

"Well, come up here an' pull a chair with us."

Earl didn't say anything. I didn't know whether Effie would want Marion hanging around. Not too much. She had plans about him all right, and I knew what. And here these two cowhands didn't seem aiming to fight about anything.

It was sure disappointing to Effie, I figured. They were friendlier than ever. Where one went the other went. If Earl went down to Gebauer's to spark Miss Frawleen maybe, he took Marion with him. Maybe just scared of Effie's plans. Marion wasn't so brash, and he didn't wear all his jingly Mexican clothes so much. He'd lost a couple of buttons off too. And he never wore them to town into Jake's place, so there must have been trouble there. Effie said Earl was likely stakin' him to a drink at Jake's an' all, an' Earl ought to be saving every dime to git married on.

Well, this night, sitting along the corral fence, Lige said to Marion, "Well, come on up. The boys had a bath already fer Thanksgivin'."

"Thanks, mebbe I will."

Thinking of that dang bath made me feel scratchy again. Two weeks now, and I didn't feel right yet. So I said to Marion, "Say, can you git a bath down at your kinfolks'? Sure, everybody gits a bath holidays comin'."

"All them kids down there in the soddy, there ain't much room as you got here. Don't worry about me an' Earl. We'll git baths in town and haircuts too."

"Fer Effie," said Earl to me, kind of solemn. "Marion takes more baths 'n you do. He ain't no heathen."

"Well, then, how come he smelled like camphor when he come up from Mexico last summer?"

Lige yelled, "Hey, you—shut up!"

Ellis yelled, "Yeh, it ain't polite to say that!"

Old Earl looked just kind of scared again as he did if anybody got to asking about Marion in Mexico. Marion he looked kinda worried too. He picked up his big Mexican hat and smelled it and shook his head.

Lige said, "Hey, don't mind Chick. He ain't much sense. An' Effie keeps pesterin' the boys all the time about . . . about . . . well, gittin' married an' all. Chick, you git to hell in the house."

Earl Staley looked more worried. Marion said, "Well, excuse me—am I interferin'?"

"Naw," said Lige. "Boy, yore welcome as birds in May." He looked around at the stars and started "Snakes in his whisky . . . "

Earl said, "I guess I'll ride a piece with Marion an' talk. About land out in Custer County now. Ain't no cow country left anywheres."

Ellis and I dragged the blankets onto the hay under the wagon. Lige went into the house. I heard him jaw Effie.

Ellis said to me, "Now you done it ag'in."

"Well, I'm just tryin' to fix things like Effie wants. Git these two dang cow waddies in a shootin' fight over Miss Worsenever. But them two fellers are about busted now, I guess; can't even buy a drink to start trouble on. All I'm tryin' to do is help Effie now an' git it all fixed up like she wants. Big weddin' with a fiddle."

"Yeh, but nobody's asked Miss Frawleen yet. Earl won't go down to Gebauer's any more unless he's got Marion along. Only time I ever seen him alone with ol' Worsenever was once they was walkin' along the South Eighty line, just talkin'. I got off an' crawled down the draw to watch 'em. Thought mebbe he'd kiss her. Dang it, they just come back talkin', an' Frawleen picked some flowers an' Earl gits on his critter an' lopes off."

"I guess it ain't goin' to be like in the book. Even Effie can't git them two boys in a fight, I bet. I guess she's dependin' on me to help out. She can't git it like her book.

It's like that story in the Reader about the dog jumpin' in the river to haul the boy out. Ain't so."

Old Bluch and Tige were beginning to crawl closer up on me in the hay, as the nights were colder. That Rachel bitch stayed with her pups at the straw barn, for under the covered wagon it was getting pretty crowded, seven pups growing up fat.

Ellis said, "Git to sleep. You aim to talk all night about Miss Frawleen an' two busted cowhands that won't git in a fight over her nohow you fix it? Thanksgivin' next week."

"Effie will start us killin' turkeys to hang an' chill. She'll have us diggin' punkins outa the hole fer pies. She'll make the whole outfit work now with no peace till it's all over."

"Git to sleep an' stop jawin' about it."

Lige went to town once more to get some spices and pie stuff. He had to figure on the Mortgage Intrust, too, in November, but he'd put that off until the last trip before big snows blew down and made travel pretty hard. Two more loads of wheat to town and the Mortgage was fixed until next year. Effie said there wouldn't be much money for Christmas, but there never was much. Nobody cared anyhow. We weren't the worryin' kind. Nobody went anywhere for holidays, and nobody came to see us. After freeze-up getting around to see folks was too much trouble and cold feet in the wagon, so we didn't know what went on around the country.

School would be out and Teacher gone home somewhere. Ellis and I hoped for a big blizzard to blow down,

and then she might not get back for an extra week. I told
Effie there was no use o' me goin' back to school, fer
I knew all the stuff. She said I could borry an Arithmetic
an' wade into that again. But I hated it and was scared
Lige would find one in town and fetch it home to make
me more trouble with multiplications.

So Thanksgiving came on pretty fine with Effie up to
her neck in work and making us all help. Earl was here
off and on. One wheat-hauling trip Lige brought us home
six apples and four oranges, and I'd never seen either but
once before in my life. That was last Christmas when he
came home with the same.

Effie gave us one apiece and shined the others up to keep
for Christmas, for she said, "Lands, the Mortgage an' all,
this may be all you boys git fer Christmas gifts!"

And it was. And we never gave the matter a thought.
Everybody must live as we did, I thought. Plenty to eat
and no worries.

Gifts? There weren't any to give. Apples and oranges
were a sort of curiosity to tell about at school. And keep
shined up as long as they would keep, and then eaten,
expectant of some strange results. Apples from Back
East. Oranges from Down South. What else lay behind
the snowdrifts piling up, getting bigger, harder as winter
came?

Pretty soon a wagon could be driven over the drifts, but
it was risky. If the wheels broke through on one side, the
outfit would tip over and drag the team into a tangle of
harness. So any road wound far off around the bigger
drifts, and there a track was made to the next house or to
town.

After winter really set in we didn't go to town. Lige said he'd like to see the *County Republican* once in a while to see what happened in politics but if a man didn't know until spring he was just as well off. Ellis and I wondered if the country had been wrecked yet and we hadn't had any hand in it. But we forgot it all with winter problems setting on us.

Thanksgiving came first. That was a week of butchering and hanging meat to chill—in the lean-to where we boys now slept, and outside on the north side of the house high up on poles out of the dogs' reach. But the cats could climb. Two hogs and a beef. Plenty for every living critter. Ellis and I ran down and captured turkey gobblers and whacked off their heads, picked them, hung them to freeze. And Effie wondered to whom we might give what we didn't need. She couldn't think of anyone who wasn't as well off as we were or even better. She was having a time with her busted cookstove and all the pies and cakes and stuff. The whole soddy smelled of spices, and menfolks squatted outside by the door, sniffing, not daring to go in while Effie was working. A whole big jar of mincemeat had been made up and put out in the snow—and the dogs got it. Effie jawed a lot, and Ellis and I chopped a lot more dried fruit and nuts and stuff for her.

Thanksgiving week was a big smelly riot of things to eat.

Marion came up, for he'd rather be with Earl and have Effie's cooking than stay at his cousin's.

The day before Thanksgiving Mr. Gebauer stopped on his way from town, twisted his big mustache free from frost and talked to Effie. When he had gone home Effie ran to us boys very excited. "It's a sign! I knew it would come about. Mr. Gebauer came to invite Earl to dinner. Miss Frawleen's first Thanksgivin' an' she gets Earl invited."

"Didn't invite Marion?"

"Nobody but Earl! It's comin' out like the book!"

"Sure as ducks Earl won't go without Marion. He'll be too scared of women chasin' him anyhow."

When Thanksgiving Day came the two cowhands rode in, all shaved up and clean, and Effie got hold of Earl alone. She talked a long time by the corral, and Earl kept shaking his head.

After a while Effie came to the soddy, plumb disgusted. Earl gave all kinds of reasons why he couldn't go to Gebauer's for dinner. Effie's cooking was the best in the county, he said, but Effie just looked glum. She whispered to me, "Look, Chick, you always got a lot of idees. Make that man go to Gebauer's somehow so Miss Frawleen won't be mad at him."

"The dang fool won't budge without Marion. He knows you're drivin' us all crazy tryin' to git him married, an' he ain't goin' to put himself in danger. Anyhow, he's busted."

"I wonder, now. Always when he came up from Texas he'd saved his wages. And he couldn't have spent all his money on that soddy out in Custer. I don't understand such a stubborn man."

Well, the six of us jammed into the soddy around the table somehow and ate turkey and stuff until it was time to whittle toothpicks outdoors.

Lige had brought a little bottle of whisky, and all the

menfolks except Ellis and me had a drink. Holidaytime
was one time when Effie allowed Lige to have a drink in
the house. But that Thanksgiving didn't go so well as
other times. Effie was aggravated because Earl didn't go
down to Gebauer's for dinner. Earl looked wild-eyed
when she urged him again and hung onto his friend like
he was desperate. Marion would have gone in a minute if
he'd been invited. I began to think for sure Effie'd have a
time getting this cowhand to go shine around Miss Frawleen unless he had Marion along.

Poor old Earl! It looked to me like all Effie was putting
on his plate was turkey necks to show him she was
mad, but Lige piled on the best meat for him and the
biggest piece of mince pie to show he was sorry for him.

When all us menfolks were outdoors out of the wind by
the straw barn and pickin' our teeth good, Marion said,
"Well, mebbe I ought to slope out o' this country an' go
down Indian Territory an' find me a winter ridin' job.
Nothin' to do up here fer a hand, an' Earl tryin' to make
himself a farm out in Custer County."

We chored and went into the soddy and helped Effie
pile and wash dishes. Rest of the Thanksgiving dinner was
dumped out in the snow for dogs and cats, and in no time
there was a roaring fight over it. Nine o'clock before the
house was straight again. Lige got his boots off behind
the sheet wall. Effie said us boys better make a bed in the
lean-to, for the weather was setting in cold. But we
dragged the old buffalo hide out to the covered wagon
again, snugged in the hay and pulled all the horse blankets
over us. We hated to sleep in the house steady for winter,
but we'd have to before first blizzard.

Out here we could talk without grownups messin' in. Ellis said, "Earl's buckin' now. He ain't set fer marryin'."

"You wait. Effie'll git Earl in a jam where he can't git out."

I wanted to talk awhile, but Ellis warmed up first so he could get to sleep. As a matter of fact we had our own mystery out at the Buffalo Waller, the great thing that had kept us cautious all fall, and with winter coming on we didn't know what to do about it. If big snows came before Christmas and we could be tracked and Lige began to miss corn and fodder from the place, we'd have to tell it all.

Lige got in only one more trip wheat-hauling. But he'd got the Intrust paid on the Mortgage, and Effie became cheerful again. She didn't pester Earl about Miss Frawleen, how she was such a fine girl even if she couldn't talk much English yet. Earl wouldn't say a word back. Marion Marlow didn't come around so much any more, but he could sneak over to Gebauer's from where his kinfolks lived nine miles over south by the crick and see Miss Frawleen, and Effie nor anybody else would know about it. Earl wouldn't talk about Marion any more either; so maybe Effie had got them two boys worked up to some fightin' trouble.

But nobody mentioned that rookus any more either. Earl and Lige took up their seven-up games again, snowed-in nights at the soddy. Effie told Ellis and me to shine up the four apples we'd got for Thanksgiving and she'd put them on a string and hang them up and they would be Christmas gifts for us. We didn't worry. Nobody else got any gifts. Christmas would be just another big dinner, but maybe before New Year's, when we'd stay up until midnight and go out and watch Lige shoot his double-barrel shotgun up to the stars, Effie'd let us eat our apples. Just now they were too red and pretty for boys to get their dirty paws on.

There they hung on a string tied to a splinter of the boards which held up the sod roof. All these grownups had seen lots of apples. Earl said back in Arkansaw sometimes they were red all over the ground under the trees. Well, maybe so. It was hard to believe. Marion said he'd seen oranges on trees down in Mexico, but when he said that Earl Staley gave him a quick, hard look as if he better shut up about Mexico. It just made me wonder about those two cowhands: somebody wasn't telling the truth. Last summer Marion had come back with a lot of money and his fine clothes and riding around mighty important. And now he was broke, holed up for winter down at his kinfolks'. And Earl was broke too, living on Lige and Effie for the winter, and they glad to have him. She did her best to have him go down to Gebauer's and shine around Miss Frawleen. And Earl scared to try it. Marion had been the boy for that when he had his money and dude clothes and could ride around hell-whoopin' in front of women, a handsome young cowhand, while Earl wasn't handsome at all. But they were both quiet now—something on their minds, and I had to find out. Maybe Effie knew something. At any rate she took those two busted hands in and treated them like they were big company like preachers maybe.

Earl said, "I ain't got a roof on my soddy yet, so it's full o' snow. Sometimes I think I better throw that claim up an' quit."

"You better not!" I yelled. "Effie'll have somethin' to

say about that! She's got plans fer you. Stay here, git married, grow with the country an' have a lot o' babies!"

"Oh, hell!" said Marion, and he looked hard at his friend. Earl gave me a terrible look.

Lige broke in, "Now, don't nobody pay attention to what Chick says. He's just a natcheral-born dang fool. Earl's a free American citizen an' a good cowhand, an' he don't have to git married or nothin' if he don't want to."

"Then he better light out fer Texas."

"I never heard such dang-fool yawp in my life," Earl said.

I said, "I guess Effie's give up the plan o' having you two fellers git in a fight over a girl, but she's hot an' heavy after a weddin'."

"Oh, hell!" Marion looked hard at Earl. "Well, excuse me. I guess I better pull south an' go ridin' fer Bill Ritter again. Winter range, but mebbe that outfit fergot me now."

That seemed funny. I said, "I thought you was ridin' for that outfit last summer, the fancy duds you got an' money till you blowed it all in. Where was you at?"

Marion didn't answer. He looked at Earl, and Earl's face kind of twitched up, but he didn't speak. Mystery again, and I knew it! Effie didn't know everything in the world! Lige he looked kind of pained now. Stopped pickin' his teeth, got up and brushed snow off his boots. "Hey, Chick, you an' Ellis! Time to get on them chores—hear me?"

And all that autumn Ellis and I had been whispering about the big secret we'd had since September. Something we couldn't tell anybody, especially cowhands. We were afraid that Earl or Marion might wander out past the Buffalo Waller and discover the big secret. The big secret was better than Indians or weddin's or anything you could think of. We were so afraid that someone might trail us to the Waller after the first little snow that we used to go away around and come in from the far side and try to make Lige think we were tracking jack rabbits. We had to steal fodder and lug water from the ranch, and Lige wondered once what we did that for, but he thought it was just some foolishment about fighting Indians, so he didn't care.

We told Effie we had to spend so much time at the Waller because we were trying to make a wooden door for the dugout, and she said if we stole another board from the lean-to she'd go out there and wreck the Waller herself. That scared us worse than ever. We just couldn't have anybody go near the Waller and find the big secret. It had started last September, the first week of this term of school, and had kept us whispering and plotting more than if we had found a real dead feller.

# 12

# The Last Longhorn

---

LIGE used to tell us, every summer, never to go off far west from the Buffalo Waller, for somewhere out there was the last range land and the last small bunch of range stock. In September it would be rounded up for the autumn drive south. He said those steers could be mean, catching a boy on foot out on the prairie, but we didn't pay much heed to what Lige said. It had been about time to think of school again, and Ellis and I thought it was a time to quit for good and all. All boys quit school when they grew bigger, and I certainly felt bigger, getting close to ten now. If we quit, we'd know we were big boys.

Lige grumbled some. "With all the teachin' you've had you don't know much yet. And think you know it all. I used to think Marion Marlow was the most conceited hellion around here, but yore conceiteder. Know so much now you want to quit school."

But Effie said no, I better whang away at arithmetic and spelling until maybe I got an inch taller and hefted heavier. Then I could quit school for good.

Ellis said, "Dang it, just fat up like me. Then you can quit."

We were out at the Waller, where we always kept stuff to eat after school, hooked from the ranch and stored until it spoiled. Now, after the great discoveries of the four road trips, we had time to work at our hidden fortress in the prairie grass. By this time we had got the ramrod twisted out of the old muskit so we could get a load of powder down, and Ellis said we ought to have another Indian attack before we got too grown to play fighting Indians. But there wasn't a thing in a mile for Indians to skulk in and attack the Waller, so we pulled a lot of big tumble-weeds and pegged them on the prairie.

Then we could yell and shoot the muskit into the line of tumbleweeds, and it was only fair to give Indians some-thing to sneak behind and shoot back at us. The first time the muskit went off a cowhand who'd been following a chuck wagon 'way over west came up to see what the heck was going on, and when we told him Indians were skulking behind the tumbleweeds he just rode off, shaking his head pretty dumb. We saw some steers 'way off, moving south, the last trail outfit ever seen around there, and everybody would be pleased, for the longhorns would get mixed up sometimes with folks' home herds and scare women, and some farmer would take a shot at them. A herd boss couldn't do much about it; there were too many farmers around for trouble these days.

Well, this hot evening, when we tried to load the muskit for another crack at Indians, Ellis got the ramrod stuck again, and, working at it, we didn't notice a storm building up northwest. It got dark early now. Big clouds rolling up and thunder and lightning. Then came a scatter of rain, and the wind whooped down. We backed into the dugout cut into the wall of the Waller, and in a minute there was the dangest thunder you ever heard! Rain came boiling in between the chinks of the sod roof. We saw lightning on the white sand of the Waller.

We knew it wouldn't last long, so we sat in the leaks. Then came the worst crack of all, and then more thunder.

Closer, and it wasn't thunder. Ellis stuck his head out of the dugout and yelled, "Duck yore head! Stampede o' steers is goin' right over the whole shebang!"

I didn't have time to yell or move in the dark before cattle were thundering on both sides and then down in the Waller and climbing up again. You just saw them by lightning streaks while you dodged.

All we knew was that the poles crashed in on us, and hoofs and noses and tails were thumping and fighting to get over the edge of the Waller. We certainly got thumped around. My eyes were chucked with sand, but it was too dark to see anyhow. I bumped into Ellis crawling out the dugout. We stood up and listened. That stampeding outfit had passed right on, and it was some quiet now. I could hear a cow feller 'way off, cussin', trying to turn that bunch, and he sounded pretty mad.

We climbed up on the rim of the Waller. Quiet now, hardly a drop of rain, and the moon was breaking through clouds off east.

Ellis yelled at that far-off cowhand, "Git out an' never come back! See what you done, them steers trompin' the dugout down on us hellity-split!" Then he went to rubbing sore spots.

I could see better now. Started to other end of the Waller when I heard something shoving around. I went closer and saw a little shine a-moving. Then I backed toward the busted dugout. "Look out! One o' them dang longhorn steers is fightin' to climb out. **Git back—he's** rarin' crazy!"

We saw his head swing. The little shiny points were moonlight on his horn tips. That critter was the biggest, skinniest bag of bones I ever saw—and the horns, I bet, were six feet tip to tip! We backed to the dugout and watched. A great big old mosshorn fighting to climb the sandbank! Once he heaved a kind of weak blat.

Ellis said, "Why, that feller ain't got strength to climb out. Somethin' wrong with his hindquarters."

We watched him struggling a long time. Then he gave it up. Swung half around and gave a sort of moan. The moon hit his eyes, and they looked funny. Cloudy white patches. I figured he was blind too. He just stood quiet, swinging his big horn spread.

But Ellis said, "Don't go close. If he charged us down in this hole, he'd knock us half a mile with them horns."

When I moved he turned his shaggy head. He wasn't completely blind, but he couldn't climb that sandbank. He backed his rump to it and stood swinging his head. We came closer, very careful.

Ellis said, "Aw, that poor ol' feller! That outfit gone on an' left him. Got old an' couldn't keep up with them devilin' young steers. Tuckered out an' give up."

I came closer. He watched me, and I bet we were the first boys he ever saw in his life. The hide on his neck was in big folds and wrinkles, and his ribs stuck out, and his face all puckered skin. His eyes were watery, as if he was bawling like a baby-kid.

We sat down on the busted dugout poles. Ellis said, "No more Texas trail for him. An' no more outfits will come back up here either, come spring. I bet that bunch o' steers didn't let him git much to eat, him kinda blind-like. I wish——"

I hollered, "Say, we got a steer now, bigger 'n anybody's got! Just fat him up some. Let's go out an' cut some grass. I got my toad stabber to cut with, an' you can pull some."

Well, we went out in the moonlight and whacked wet grass. Pretty tough hay in September. We lugged an armful into the Waller and shoved it as close to his nose as we dared with his horns swinging and him giving a snort or two as he backed away. Ellis got the water bucket we always lugged from the ranch and shoved it close and scooted back. One swipe of those horns would have knocked him dead. Then we watched. He wouldn't eat or drink. Pretty soon he swayed and laid down on his side and heaved like a sigh. Just had to rest. Once he twitched an ear as if listening to see if the cowhands and the whole roundup had really gone off and left him to die.

We went home and caught heck for not doing chores. And didn't tell anybody about the stampede in the dark. Somebody would shoot Ol' Longhorn if he got out. He wasn't good for anything, hide, tallow or meat. Just bone and gristle. But they'd shoot him if he went around the little tame home herds folks had.

We got out early next day before anybody, filled a sack with corn and lugged two buckets of water. We wondered if he'd got out and tried to follow the outfit. But there he was, come sunup. Looked bigger than ever but gant and wrinkled, on his feet again. He gave us a bad look when we slid down at our end of the Waller. Swinging his big horns, watching us. We sidled near as we dared and threw the corn. We put the buckets half to him and scooted back. He wouldn't eat while we were there, so we climbed out and went to the Indian skulkin' place. After a while I skulked back and looked over the edge. He was nearing the corn. Got an ear and then saw me. He stopped and backed as if getting ready to charge. Then he eyed me a long time and picked up the corn. Then another ear, but very hostile to us.

Ellis said, "We better git back for breakfast an' ready for school. Don't tell anybody about him. Mebbe if he eats good a few days he can climb up that sandbank. Try to foller his outfit—but he'd git shot by some farmer scared of longhorns."

"An' if he starts fer Texas an' deep snow comes when he's down in the creek timber country, he'll get wolf-dragged, weak as his legs is. I don't aim to have wolves or anybody worry him. Tonight we'll lug some fodder out. It's goin' to be a job, luggin' water an' all till he gets some strength."

"Yeh, an' we got to fix up the dugout right in front his nose, an' he won't like that."

We hoofed to the Waller after school. He was right there on his legs. We cut grass and shoved near him. He just watched like a snake looks. Then we went to digging the cottonwood poles out of the wreck that stampede had made, and we kept an eye on him, very cautious. I guess he'd never heard boys talking or seen any kind of house, and he was puzzled. But he didn't charge. Once in a while he would pick up some grass, stop chewing and watch us. It made us pretty nervous, for, if he started, we couldn't get out in time. But he didn't. Near dark, when we went home late for chores, we got jawed some. But we thought of the old red steer.

Well, it went on that way a week or two. Effie wondered where the water buckets were gone so much, and Lige asked was we luggin' fodder off to build another skulk hole for Indians. We got dang tired rustling feed for that old steer. But he wouldn't fat up; like me, he just stayed skinny. But he didn't watch us so hostilely. Now he'd eat right while we were working to sod over our dugout, maybe not two rods from his horns, and he never started. Once I reached a fodder stalk to his nose, and he ate it.

We found tracks where he'd been right up close to the dugout, but when we came he'd swing back to his end of the Waller and face out with them swinging horns. Ellis said he must be getting more strength, maybe sassy-like afterwhile. Dang hard to be friendly with that old feller, him always backed in his corner watching us, wondering what we was up to in the dugout. We couldn't play fighting Indians any more, yelling and shooting from the fort out to the tumbleweeds, for the big steer would be behind our backs and maybe get excited. And, the colder the weather got, the more he ate—without getting a pound of meat on him, it seemed to us.

"What we goin' to do, deep snow comes and we've got to dig fodder outa shock an' fetch it 'way out here? An' water freeze in the buckets worse 'n it does at school?"

"I dunno what. Ol' Longhorn ain't seen nothin' all his life in winters but snow an' have to paw under it fer grass, a range critter like him. Come Christmas we bring him extry big feed anyhow, the Waller snowed in mebbe."

Well, in December the first blizzard hit. It came whooping down one afternoon, and in a minute the schoolhouse windows were full of hard-packing blizzard snow and the wind like to jerked the roof off. Everybody was more or less used to blizzards out in that prairie country, but getting caught in school was something nobody'd figured on. The teacher said it wasn't any use for anyone to think of getting home. Maybe some man would come with a wagon for us all, and maybe not. This was a bad one. In half an hour the school was almost dark except for the little coal-stove front.

Everybody got around it and talked and laughed. Prairie boys and girls don't get scared easy. We just listened to the wind outside and over the roof and that hard snow snapping when it hit wood.

But Ellis and me got to thinking. Lige had a bad cold and sniffles, and on a night like this he'd need help taking care of the stock to keep them from drifting off to die somewhere. So Ellis said, "Say, I bet we can make it home. Git to that little line o' cottonwoods along West Eighty line an' foller it right close to the ranch."

"Yeh. Ought to help Lige, an' anyhow I don't want to be cooped up here all night with bunch o' little kids an' two women."

Ellis grinned and grabbed the doorknob. When he jerked it open snow came whirling clear to Teacher's desk. I heard her scream. But Ellis was out. Me after him, and Miss Frawleen yelled and grabbed at me, but I was too quick. We headed off and in a minute couldn't see a thing except snow. Not even the schoolhouse right behind us. I saw Ellis' red muffler and grabbed the end. We both yelled but couldn't hear each other. Ellis found the end of the cottonwood row, little saplings bent over in packing snow. On we went, and Lige would certainly be surprised when we tumbled into the soddy, and him with chills maybe.

Then Ellis stopped, and I stumbled up to him. I couldn't see any more cottonwoods. But we hunted the next one flat under snow. Ellis yelled, "Hang to me, Smarty! Foller this line an' we'll git right home."

"Sure! Go ahead. I'm follerin'!"

But it was hard. Once the wind threw Ellis flat. When he got up he didn't know which was east, and where was the line of cottonwoods. Ellis felt for one and yelled again.

Then I knew that boy was lost. He couldn't tell directions except by the wind, and it was tricky. He yelled something and headed right into it. Then I let go his muffler, for it was choking him. He came back, and we both scrooged down in the snow. It blew right out from under our knees. He yelled, "Come on, Chick—can't stay here!"

He battled on slow, and I follered—right into that white wall, and it was darkening fast. I yelled, "Mebbe we better bed down like a jack rabbit an' let snow cover us."

"We'd be froze dead afore mornin'. Let's try again while we got strength. Come on!"

I shoved after him, and a shift of wind threw me. I felt something scratching my face, and then I dug lower and yelled, "Looky, this is the Indians' skulkin' line we built!"

He crawled around and felt. A flattened-out tumbleweed, sure, tied down as we had fixed them. Ellis got up and yelled, "Well, of all things! Go straight north an' hit the Waller. Crawl in the dugout, an' I bet there's side meat left in the box. An' wind won't hit us down in the Waller!"

So on he went and I after him. Well, the wind got worse. We couldn't stand against it. We crawled in and over drifts just whirling in our eyes. Then I fell over something straight on my head in the snow. The rim of the Waller! Ellis came tumbling after me. We twisted around and stood up. Flapped our hands to warm them and stomped our feet. The bottom of the Waller was about six feet under, and the wind just leveled across over our heads.

We stood there, yelling, happy as spring meadow larks.

"Got matches in the dugout!"

"Got some bread, too, left from last week. Boy, we made it safe!"

In a minute we weren't so sure. The Waller was drifted almost full. But we'd dig into the dugout. Couldn't see to the other end where the big steer kept himself. I wondered how he was making out. He'd been in blizzards all his life, but he was old and weak now, even with all the feed we'd lugged him.

When we got to the dugout end we couldn't see a thing, it was so dark. Ellis found the end of a roof pole, and it was caved down. The dugout was full of snow packed harder than anywhere else. The roof was down under

the weight too. I went to digging and touched some hair.
I felt all around, and it was warm skin. I yelled at Ellis,
"Hey, here's Ol' Longhorn down on his side right chuck in
the dugout door!"

We both felt into his snow-packed ribs, and his skin
twitched and wiggled. We'd never laid hand on him
before. I crawled right over him, and then we knew the
dugout was no manner of use to us. Caved in and snow-
packed. Ellis crawled over Ol' Longhorn, and a sweep of
wind threw him again. He laid there and yelled something. I stooped down by him and found myself right
against the steer's belly, and it was warm and fine. I felt
his hindquarter, and he never kicked. His skin twitched, as
if he was trying to mean, "Hole up! Git warm!"

Well, I husked my frozen mittens and did warm my
hands against his belly's short hair, and Ellis wormed
around so we had heads near together. Ellis whooped,
"Say, he had more sense 'n we did! Laid down an' let snow
drift over him."

"First time I ever knew him to come up to the dugout.
Mebbe he tried to git in. But them horns wouldn't let
him."

"Mebbe he come tryin' to see if we was in the dugout,
an' wonderin' if we'd bring fodder tonight."

After that we got quiet. Ellis yelled once not to go to
sleep, for that's when you'd freeze, people said. Nobody
around there had a thermometer, as they called it, so
nobody knew how cold it was until somebody got to
town, maybe a month later, and was told at the store it had
been thirty below or something. I didn't care, with my
back against Longhorn's warm hide and my frozen boots

jammed between his hind legs and my hands in his hair.
If I moved too much, he'd wiggle his skin, but he never
broke the snow crust that piled over all of us. I didn't
hear much wind now. And I went to sleep finally, my
hands warmed inside my shirt; and the last thing I thought
was that Effie would suppose we'd stayed at school and
mind Teacher, so the folks at the ranch wouldn't worry.
So I didn't worry. I went to sleep, my back warm against
Longhorn but pretty cold in front.

The next I knew was Ellis crawling and humping snow
with his back and pulling snow down from the hole he'd
made until he could stand up. Then he kicked me in the
side. "Hey, Chick, git up! Wind ain't so big. Looks like
sun's breakin' out east. Ol' blizzard wasn't long, but she
was a snorter! You froze stiff? I bet it was forty below!"

"I bet she's a hundert. I'm too stiff to move. You wait."

I shoved my hands back against Longhorn's belly for
another warmup, for they were mighty cold. I dug fingers
into snowy hair to his hide, and it never wiggled back to
me. I felt all along his snow-packed belly, and it was cold
as my hands. I crawled along and dug my hands to his
neck, and all the time Ellis was yelling at me to get out of
the hole we'd slept in. Ellis was a lot taller than me and
could see over the drifts.

"Hurry up! We'll git home an' warm an' eat an' bring
a shovel back to dig Ol' Longhorn out if he's too weak to
fight back."

He ain't fightin' no more, I grumbled to myself.

I crawled up and stood beside Ellis. Our heads were
above the snow pack, and we saw a thin little sun fighting
in the flying scud. Snow everywhere. Once I saw Lige's

windmill when the wind didn't whirl so much, but I knew the soddy must be buried clear over the roof. Ellis was yelling as if he was happy, pounding his mittens to warm up, but I didn't say anything.

The sun brightened a little and I saw it shine on one tip of horn maybe an inch above the snow. Ellis said, "What's the matter, Chick? Face froze or somethin', you can't talk?"

"Don't wanta talk. Ol' Longhorn's dead."

Ellis twisted around in the snow, startled.

"Go feel of him. Froze stiff an' dead, mebbe too old to stand any more."

Ellis dug down and felt along the snow-packed belly hair. Right where we'd bedded against him were two spots like nests. Ellis got up and muttered, "Dead, all right. The pore ol' feller!"

We climbed out of the Waller and looked back. Just one little shiny tip of his horns was above the drift.

Ellis said, "Look, we'd froze last night if it hadn't been for him."

"Sure would. We . . . I . . . I guess we better start fer the ranch, Effie bein' worried. Come day, Lige'd git to the school an' we wouldn't be there. Teacher'd tell him we started home. He'll be huntin' fer us under the drifts— dead."

"Come on home. Got to warm up ag'in, standin' in this wind."

Ellis followed me, but he looked back. "Say, I hate to think of him not bein' here when we cut across from school to the dugout every day to see how he's doin'."

"Yeah. Say, we'd been dead too if we hadn't built them

weeds up fer Indians to skulk in. They led us to the Waller."

"Yeah. Then the ol' steer kept us alive all night. Come on."

We battled on, pretty cold. Sometimes a drift wouldn't hold, and then we went down above our heads. But we were dry and hadn't worn our strength out last night trying to travel on. That's why people die in snow. Get in a sweat and then it freezes next your skin and you lose your strength fighting wind. We knew better, but it was Old Longhorn's belly warmth that saved us.

The snow glitter blinded us, but I saw smoke over the drifts and knew it was from the soddy. Then I saw some people over south and then a stalled wagon in a drift. But Ellis and I kept on toward the snow-buried soddy. I got to thinking of hot cakes and coffee and getting cussed for ever leaving the schoolhouse. Then I fell over the edge of a little draw, and bunch grass frozen hard as a club hit me over the ear. Seems I didn't know much after that except that Ellis, up to his shoulders in a drift, was yelling and waving. Then I heard somebody crunching in the snow. It was Earl Staley hauling me to my feet and wiping snow from my eyes. Ellis was talking to Miss Frawleen, and she looked to me about nine feet high in the sun glitter.

Earl grabbed me off my feet. "Come on, you smarty! I always said you ain't no sense, boys forkin' into the blizzard last night! Gebauer an' me made it to the schoolhouse this mornin' an' everybody was safe but you two!"

"How's Lige an' his chills? We started home to help."

"Lige in bed with shakes sure enough. Come on home."
Miss Worsenever smiled and said, " 'Ello, Smarty!"

So we all snow-dragged and waded and got to the ranch, and, sure enough, there were hot cakes and coffee and everyone cussing us out. Well, I went to considering: Miss Frawleen starts off with Earl to find us maybe dead, and here we are eating hot cakes. Lige sat up in bed and smoked and croaked. Effie had his neck all tied around with flannel soaked in kerosene.

When we got thawed out some over the cob fire Lige said, "I don't see yet why you didn't freeze night like that. So you got to the Waller an' bedded down outa the wind? That was more sense 'n I thought you had. Still I don't understand."

"Wasn't the Waller exactly. Was a big ol' longhorn we had in there, an' he warmed us up an' then died, dang it."

Effie said, "Now what's this yarn? Range cattle near us?"

Ellis said, "You womenfolks needn't be scared no more! The last outfit an' last cowman went hellin' south last September an' never'll come back no more."

"Thank my stars," said Effie. "You kept a steer in the Waller?"

"Yeh. He had weak back or somethin'. Couldn't git out, so we fed him."

Lige said, "I wondered where my corn shocks were goin' last two months. Soon's I git over shakes we'll all go out an' see that critter."

"Savin' us this way, he ought to have a reg'lar funeral," I said.

When the drifts settled and froze so we could travel the tops, Lige went out with us. The snow had melted a little, but all we could see of Ol' Longhorn was just the tips of his horns shining in the sun. We went home and left him all winter, and when spring thaws came there was his old scraggy head with the eyes open and his horns barring the dugout door as if he aimed to keep everybody out except Ellis and me, being his friends.

Effie and Earl and Miss Frawleen went out when the ground settled so a wagon could travel. Lige stood on the rim of the Waller, staring down at the big red steer like a man studying.

"He come to you boys in storm, an' he passed away in storm. Ol' fightin' Texas longhorn. I'll mule-drag him out, an' you boys can dig a big hole. Give him a Christian buryin' for a fact."

And that's what happened. Earl came out and helped dig, though he was hanging around Gebauer's now more than he ought to. But Effie said he wasn't saying a word about getting married. Too scared to talk real business. Before we buried Ol' Longhorn farm people came from miles around to see that steer. His horns were a mighty sight when Earl cut them off and nailed them above our dugout door after we got it fixed up again. An old retired cowhand from over by Plum Creek looked Longhorn all over and never found a brand or rope mark on him. He'd been a fighting maverick all his days, following trail herds but keeping clear of cowhands and roundups. Must have been a mean one.

Effie said, "Mebbe so. But these boys were the only friends he ever had in all his born days. He knew they were draggin' fodder clear out there because they were his friends."

I said, "Well, he certainly was good to us."

Ellis said, "Wisht we could have saved him until new spring grass had come. Been like that sarsapiller tonic you want us to take to tone up a feller's blood like."

"The pore ol' critter!" said Effie. "Just goes to show there ain't nothin' clear bad in the world if yore kind enough to it. Git some dry cobs fer the stove an' I'll make big doughnuts today."

"Yeh," said Lige. "An' I think Earl an' Frawleen saved you from freezin' in that drift. Next time you see her you be polite; anyhow, say 'Much obliged.' "

Well, I did when I saw her at school, but I said it low so as not to start any trouble with anybody. I guess she heard, though, for she smiled. That spring term was just like last year except that Ellis and I stuck it longer after we heard Lige say now we were big enough to help in field work. I didn't think I weighed a pound more, but I was hard all over, just gristle, and Ellis was growing bigger all the time. Effie was like me, brown and wiry but singing little pieces of songs she could remember from Back East. Prairie country was pretty in the spring, all little wild pink roses in green grass and the meadow larks and quail calling everywhere.

Sure enough, Lige got Ellis and me into real work—all the land he'd got into oats and barley besides corn and wheat. Ellis could handle a cultivator now, and I could follow a harrow team, which meant' just walking all day. But Lige wasn't hard on boys or horses. Half the time he had the outfit stopped to rest, and we squatted down in the black soil, listening to him tell war yarns about Vicksburg and how grand my father had looked with black young whiskers and a sword, just like the picture in Effie's trunk which she was keeping until I grew up and had a little sense, she said.

# 13

# Johnny Reb's Cap

EARL pulled out for Custer County this spring with his two cayuses and the old pack mule he'd traded one of his guns for. Maybe he really was getting a sod house up and roofed, but I didn't see how he'd do any first breakin' on prairie land without a plow. He got so he didn't talk much to anybody except Marion, who hadn't gone south for a spring job with some outfit as he always had done before. I didn't know what was on his mind either.

Ellis and I went to the Waller some days, and other days we helped Lige, and he got all his corn laid by before the Fourth of July, the last cultivating. Then he and Ellis took a load of wheat away off to a new gristmill down Plum Creek, but I stayed home because Ol' Tops was doing poorly, sometimes not wanting to get on his feet to eat. So I lugged water and hay out to him in the east pasture eighty. Effie said Tops and the old covered wagon were last relics of their start to Californy and we had to care for them. Wasn't much left of the wagon canvas by now and not much git-up-and-go to Ol' Tops's bones. Effie and I nursed him along.

But now, Fourth of July coming, Effie let me wear the little Rebel cap which she always kept in her trunk along with my father's picture in the gilt frame. Fourth of July she'd hang that picture on the wall, all shined up. The day before the Fourth I had to go west after two yearlings which the Webels said were mixed with their stock, and after I got them started toward home Harry Webel began picking on me about the Johnny Reb cap. Once I'd worn it to school and got into a fight with the Webel boys. I said a Colonel was bigger than a General. They said I was a liar. Then they had called on Teacher, and that woman had just stood there and said a general was the biggest, and that made me pretty mad. And now when Harry saw me wearing the little gray cap again he knocked it off and I lit into him. Out in the road where I'd headed our yearlings, he rassled me down, and I gouged his eye. Then he chewed my ear till it bled. All the Webel dogs began to bark, and Mrs. Webel came out and pulled Harry off me.

I started for home, but I yelled back they were all a bunch of ignorants like Teacher, who didn't know about Colonels. It was dark when I passed the schoolhouse, so I headed north to the Buffalo Waller to get a rag to mop blood off my face so Effie wouldn't see it and jaw me some. Anyhow, Lige and Ellis wouldn't come back with the grist until late, and Effie would care for Ol' Tops if he wasn't on his feet again. As for the milking and other chores, to heck with them until Ellis came back.

So it was full starry dark when I reached the Waller. I'd never been out there alone in full dark, and somehow it looked kind of scary. I got the Civil War muskit from the dugout and stacked it below the big steer's horns. On the Fourth Ellis and I always played Rebels were attacking us instead of Indians. The rim of the Waller was a breastwork, and I sat down on it, listening. A coyote was yapping somewhere, and it sounded lonesome. Made me lonesome. I wished Ellis was back with a bunch of fire-crackers Lige had promised us and some powder to load the muskit and shoot it at sunrise. But now, all alone in the dark, I started to play Johnny Reb as we'd done before; though now, being nearly ten, I felt pretty old to pretend like that when I knew better.

I walked around the breastworks, and once in a while I'd holler, "Halt! Who goes there? Advance an' give the countersign!"

That's what Lige said to do. He could tell more things about the Civil War than anybody, though he'd never been in it but one year on account of his asthmy, which made a sound like an old horse with heaves sometimes when he got talking good to Ellis and me. That Western country had a lot of men who'd been in the war, breaking up prairie to farm. Ellis and I traded with other boys for old stuff they had, bayonets and knapsacks, and we stowed it out in the dugout under the bank of the Buffalo Waller. But nobody around there could say he had a Colonel in his family, or even a Captain. That's what got me in so many fights and licked so many times, being so skinny-like. But I'd sail into 'em even if they were thirteen like Harry.

I'd take the Joggerfee book which had maps and point out all the places in Alabamy and everywhere south where my father'd gone ahead chasing Rebels out so General Sherman could march right on with no worry. Uncle Lige backed me right up too, and Effie'd laugh, washing dishes in the soddy, cold nights, and say, "Chick, put on your Johnny cap an' march! But don't go fightin' the war at school. Land, I have to mend yore pants an' wamus every week, too, you wrastlin' bull calves around the corral pertendin' they's cavalry Rebels an' all. Lige, you quit tellin' all that stuff to the boys. Chick'll git tromped sometime chasin' mean steers with that ol' bayonet, jabbin' their ribs an' yellin' fer 'em to surrender."

Then Ellis—he didn't have a Colonel in his family—had put in, "Chick'll git his head knocked off, braggin' at school."

Maybe I did brag too much even if I was too skinny to fight well. But didn't I have the picture in the gold frame hanging on the wall on the Fourth, the Colonel with big black whiskers and a sword and a big sash and a lot of brass buttons? I didn't remember ever seeing him, but there he was, pretty fierce.

Now, sitting on the breastwork, I took off the Johnny Red cap to see if I'd got blood on it from my chawed ear. Must have been a mighty small Rebel who wore that cap, for it almost fit me. It was flat on top and ragged a little, with a couple of little brass artilleries in front which I kept shined up fine. Inside on a leather band were two letters cut into it. J.J. they were, and some snowed-in nights at the soddy, me and Lige talking big, he'd say that J.J. stood for General Joe Johnston, the Confederate feller, and then I'd say that was the one my father had chased clear into the ocean and grabbed his cap and fetched it home for me.

Ellis would be melting snow for dishwater so we didn't have to go clean out to the windmill in the wind for a pailful, and Effie would be clearing the table, but she'd stop and laugh when Lige and me went to talking big about war and Indians or anything else to brag about. Snowed-in nights last winter, Earl not there to play seven-up with Lige,

him and me certainly had some big talks. All about Vicksburg, and sometimes I'd get sleepy listening to how he had
to go home after that on account of his heaves and met
Effie and got married. I got kind of sleepy now, listening
to the wind in the grass.

Well, tonight I didn't feel so big, all alone in the Waller.
Little cool wind was blowing, so I snuggled down inside
the breastwork. That coyote certainly made a lonesome
sound. I heard the grass rustling, and it was lonesome
sound too. When I could see a lantern off by the ranch
I'd know Lige and Ellis were home. Then I'd head for the
light and see folks again. I wasn't scared now, but the grass
slithered like somebody was walking in it soft like Indians.

I looked out over the breastwork. Grass rustled a little
bigger. Someone was coming outa the prairie. I wasn't
scared. Nobody around there had a Colonel in their
family, but I didn't have no family. Just the Colonel, and
him a picture. Well, something like a shadow moved
closer. Little feller not much bigger 'n Harry, thirteen
maybe. Now I wasn't scared. I just said, low and business-
like, "Halt! Who goes there!"

I heard laughing, low like grass moving. "Who be ye?"

"Folks around here know who I be. Who you?"

The feller came closer, I almost made out his face, and
he laughed. "Well, I know who you be. Fact is, yore the
Colonel's boy, an' we been figgerin' a long time how to
catch you alone. Had to talk to you. Fact is, you got my
cap."

Now, that was crazy. I just laughed. "An' fact is, the
feller that wore this cap is dead. General Joe Johnston, an'
my father——" I stopped. Somethin' funny about this fel-

ler. I wasn't scared, but I didn't want to touch him, like you wouldn't try to touch a shadow. I just grumbled, "If my father was alive, he'd give you facts. Him chasin' Joe Johnston. But he's dead a long time."

This feller just shook laughing. "Ain't it the trewth! Colonel's dead, an' what difference that make? I'm dead too!"

Well, that made me mad. I took a step and yelled, "You dead? You ain't no more dead 'n our ol' tomcat!"

"Boy, I been gone off this-yere earth nigh ten years. Malary, down in Louisiany, where I retreated. Never did surrender. Last Johnny Reb hid out in the swamps an' never did surrender."

Well, I just listened, considering. This feller was lying an' bragging maybe near as good as I could. I just hooted at him.

When I walked closer he didn't seem any nearer somehow. An' he didn't back up either, just seemed kind of wavery when the wind rustled the grass. But I was close enough to see better. He looked kind of ganted up and pale, but he was like a boy. Looked young, maybe thirteen like Harry. But I couldn't say why he seemed queer. I wasn't scared. I said, "See here, that's a whopper you tell. A Johnny Reb, an' dead too. You're clean fitified in the head. Look out!"

He was reaching for my cap. Funny about that. He touched my ear, but I didn't feel anything. But I backed away from him. He wasn't laughing now. Just said, sorry-like, "Well, sir, I'll prove it."

He turned around and seemed to be looking at the stars.

A long time, not saying a word. I began to feel mighty queer somehow. I heard something coming. Kind of a clinkety-clank, and then there was a bigger shadow in the grass. This feller put his hand down so his sword didn't bang his boots, and his face came right out plain to me. Dang if I didn't see brass buttons and a big sash and straps on his shoulders, and then big black shiny whiskers. Just like my father's picture back at the soddy. It just made me dumb, but so excited that I stuttered.

The little feller said, "Hello, Colonel! I knew if I put the call you'd come. Yore boy don't believe me." He turned to me. "Now what you say? Now go on braggin' an' blowin' about the cap!"

My father looked at me grave-like. He said in a deep sorry voice, "I know. Yes, it's come to me what he tells people."

Then he just looked at me. I blinked at him. The Colonel all right, only young, for the skin above his black whiskers was smooth, not a wrinkle on it. Both young, but the Johnny was kind o' beat-up, as if he'd had a tough time fighting Union men.

Well, I was sure skittered inside. This proved it, the whiskers and all. I didn't believe in no dang ghosts, for when Lige got to gabbing about 'em he told such tall ones that Effie made him shut up. These couldn't be no dang ghosts, for they didn't scare me, and they didn't wear white sheets and groan like Lige claimed.

But they were dead all right, for here was my father, just like the picture taken in 1865 when he took his sword and got married. Here he was, big and dignified in a uniform, but the little Johnny Reb wore some kind of ragged butternut coat, and I knew he'd never been a General or even Corp'ral. But he was laughing again.

Well, I didn't know what to say, my father looking at me so long and quiet. Effie'd always told us if we were interduced to folks we ought to be polite. So I mumbled, "Much obliged," but they didn't pay any heed to me.

"Tell him, Colonel, how you got the cap. An' it wasn't General Joe Johnston's cap, an' you never run him into the ocean when you was with Sherman, did you?"

"Certainly not. I remember distinctly how I got the cap. It was at Vicksburg after Pemberton surrendered. I found the cap outside the Confederate works and took it as a souvenir. My son must have got it somehow among my things after I passed on."

Then I got in my say at last. "Looky, inside the band it says J.J., an' if that ain't Joe Johnston, who the heck is it?"

"You heard your dad, didn't you? He found my cap just where I lost it. Alabamy field artillery—that was me. The Yanks blew up Redoubt Six, left o' Pemberton's earthworks. I was blowed up too, an' I lit out runnin'. Lost my cap sure—J.J. means Private John Jebb, not Joe Johnston, an' you know it, Colonel!"

"Yes, yes," said my father gravely. "And I picked up the cap the next day—after the surrender, Private Jebb."

Well, them two standing there talking old wartimes when they'd never seen each other in the land of the living took the wind out of me. I pushed the cap down on my chawed ear and just stuttered.

This Jebb just kind of wavered around in a dance, jeering at me. "Now, you see, all the braggin' an' lyin' you done at school an' all. The Colonel don't like it, that's what, ner me either."

My father said, "Give him his cap, son."

I took it off, and the Johnny Reb reached, and it was just a little wind moving the cap, and there it was on his head. I just grumbled, "Well, all right. But tomorry's Fourth o' July, an' Lige is bringin' some firecrackers, an' I wanted to wear the cap an'——"

"Fourth of July, at Vicksburg, 1863," said the Colonel. "Yes, that was the day Pemberton surrendered, the day I found the Rebel cap, Private Jebb."

"Yes, but I didn't surrender with Pemberton. Started runnin', you might say, but just a retreat to me. Never stopped my retreat till I was 'way down deep in Louisiany swamps, but I never surrendered. Hull Lincoln gov'ment couldn't dig me out. An' passed peaceable after you did, Colonel. Malary fer me."

"I never quite got over wounds from Allatoona, with Corse's Brigade. And, contrary to my son's story that I led Sherman's army from Atlanta to the sea, I followed it in a mule cart among the black camp followers who cared for me well. And, Jebb, I passed on, and my son couldn't possibly know a thing about me."

The Colonel looked gravely at me again, and that was awful to hear. That he'd never run General Johnston up to his neck in the ocean and grabbed his cap. I just felt fitchered out of words. My father looked as if he was longing to touch me and wouldn't.

I didn't want to touch him either, him in the big uniform and me barefooted in denim pants and a busted ear.

I just didn't say anything. This little Johnny Reb was the one who strutted about, cap on his head and eying everything. Then he said, "Say, who built this-yere earthwork? Dang if it ain't better 'n some o' Pemberton's defenses back o' Vicksburg."

He looked at me, and for the first time my father smiled. That perked me up, and I yelled, "Nobody dug it! Just ol' buffaloes scratchin' their hides mebbe million years ago, Lige said!"

"Well, I fought in worse." The Johnny grinned. "An' lemme tell you, it wasn't true what No'then folks said about us at Vicksburg—that people were so starved they ate boiled cats an' dogs. Catfish—that's it, an' I was in the defense an' know it."

My father almost laughed. I didn't want to argue with this Jebb any more. So while he pranced up and down the breastworks as if he'd captured them from me, I didn't say a word. The moon was rising slow and big off east, and my father was looking at it. Then he said quietly, "My boy, I hope you don't tell such stories about me any more. Nor do any lying at all. Nor swearing. Nor stealing things at the ranch, where they're good to you. I know. We who have passed away have means of knowing if we care to use the power given us. Mostly we don't; it's better not to return here at all. Do you understand, my son?"

"Yeh. Quit lyin'. Quit cussin'. Quit hookin' cookies an' stuff from Effie. Quit fightin', me bein' too little anyhow. Quit——"

My father did laugh softly, and just then Private Jebb came back, still eying the breastworks critically, and suddenly he looked east at the big moon. I saw them both better in moonlight but still kind of wavery in the grass. Mr. Jebb said, "We better go now."

The Colonel said something, and the two seemed to walk or maybe just float along the breastworks. I was below the top by the muskit when they came closer, kind of foggy now in the moonlight. Sure as I'm telling this, they were talking about me.

Mr. Jebb said, "It ain't so much the cap; it's all this lyin' an' braggin' the boy does about it, an' about us Johnnies bein' chased around so. I know in this-yere Hereafter you an' me got into, you ain't expected to do no cussin', but I can make remarks. An' the Great Power moved me to come. An' moved me to call on you on account o' yore boy an' his big talk. He ain't yet fitten to wear a Johnny Reb cap."

"No, Private Jebb, he isn't. And now we'll call upon the Great Power to stop him. He should believe that I was just an unknown officer of Wisconsin volunteer infantry who was with Sherman's Western Army four years. I think now he'll have the idea. Jebb, it's getting rather light, isn't it?"

"I reckon we better pull out fer Hereafter right soon."

Well, I listened and didn't know what to do. I didn't want them to go, and I got a bit creepy about having them around come daylight. I could see they didn't want to touch me, and I sure didn't want to touch them. But a feller ought to shake hands or something when another feller goes away for good and all. Effie said to be polite best we could. So I stuck my head above the breastworks and hollered, "Hey, how about some coffee?"

Well, the two just stopped wavering in the moonlight. Then Jebb said, "Say, Colonel, that sounds good. Thank ye kindly, boy."

The Colonel said something, but I didn't hear good. I just ducked down in the dugout and twisted hay for a fire and put the coffeepot over the irons and grabbed the tin cups. Still heard them talking, I guess about me and Vicksburg, it being Fourth now.

I pulled the two rusty bayonets we used for fire irons out of the ashes and put them in the box. I took two cups of coffee out on the breastworks, and it was good and hot. This would prove it to me. Lige had said all ghosts could do was groan and rattle chains and wear white sheets and, being flimsy-like, they couldn't drink coffee. Now, the Colonel and Mr. Jebb weren't that way. They must have put on their old war clothes for me so I wouldn't be scared. And they looked young and happy. The Colonel looked kind but so dignified—the whiskers, and the tassel on his hat, and a sword. I thought Mr. Jebb and I could get on better, he wearing old duds like me.

Well, I put the coffee and sugar down on the breastworks and ducked back into the dugout to see if I couldn't find some of Effie's sody biscuits for them. I heard Mr. Jebb say, "Power o' faith, Colonel. We couldn't come back to talk to yore boy if we didn't have faith we could. Power fer a message, that's what."

"Yes, Private Jebb, it takes great faith to come back. It isn't done often, and a very good thing it isn't. The scheme we know is too big for us to explain to the living. We don't know it all ourselves. But I'm very glad to be in the Hereafter. Very glad."

"Ain't it so? I wouldn't be back in land o' the livin' on no account. Folks here don't know what they're missin'."

I couldn't find a biscuit. So I just yelled "Coffee!" Then I heard the Colonel say, "Sugar, Private Jebb?" Heard a spoon tinkle. Heard little whispers-like. Waited a minute and stuck my head up. Almost day now. Heard first meadow lark singing. East was red over the prairie. Didn't see a sign of those two. Just rustling grass for miles and miles. Like soft little whispers to me.

I looked all around and hollered, "Good-by!" But didn't hear a thing except breeze in the grass and the meadow lark. I guess the Colonel and Mr. Jebb didn't want me to see which way they pulled out for Hereafter. So I went back in the dugout and sat by the dirt wall. Hadn't had a wink o' sleep all night, it seemed, but now it came on me, and the next I knew was a wallop across my sore ear and a big bang in my hair. Dugout was full o' smoke and dust, and there was Ellis up on the breastwork, looking anxious.

"Hey, Chick, why didn't you come home last night?"

"Never mind. What you chunk a firecracker down on me fer? I ought to cuss, but I ain't goin' to no more."

"Yeh? You must be dang sick then."

"Ain't sick. But you slam a firecracker down on me——"

"Well, it's Fourth, ain't it?"

I crawled out. "I bet you shot all my share o' them firecrackers. I ain't had much sleep. Had a funny night, that's what."

Well, I sat down and told him the whole thing. Ellis just grinned, not believing a word, me having such a name for telling whoppers. He just wasn't interested. Went to chunking firecrackers again. Then he saw the two cups on the breastwork. "Couple o' cowhands ride in an' you fixed coffee fer 'em?"

"No. It was the Johnny Reb feller come fer his cap. You look—it ain't anywhere."

"Of all the dang yarns I ever heard!"

"Look—just look everywhere!"

Ellis looked in the dugout and out. He knew I'd have that cap right by me if I wasn't wearing it Fourth of July. Then he came back. "Aw, you dropped it out in the grass an' some thievin' cayote grabbed it an' sneaked off."

"Yeh? Well, how about them two coffee cups out here?"

Ellis went an' looked. "Empty, dang if they ain't. But you tellin' me this yarn, I can prove yore lyin'. Ghosts can't drink coffee. They ain't got any insides. They'd leak everywhere. You must been walkin' an' talkin' in yore sleep an' now got somethin' big to tell me happened. Loco as a crazy cow."

Well, I didn't argue. I just felt sleepy and queer and kept listening to the whisper of grass in the wind. Ellis went on jeering at me. "Aw, Lige an' Effie told you so much about them ol' war battles yore dad was in that now yore all mixed up. You think too much that I call just crazy loco."

Maybe so. I quit talking and went to chunking firecrackers before Ellis used my pack up. Wasn't any use to tell anybody, so I never did. But I sure quit cussing and all. It was a fine Fourth with white clouds in blue sky and little pink roses everywhere. But before we went to the ranch I took the two coffee cups off the breastwork, and I saw sugar spilled. There were two little faint trails in the dew on the dust. Ellis'd say, just two pinchy bugs walking home from the fort. But I got down and smelled the tracks. Coffee, all right. Maybe they did leak. Two little damp trails heading south into the prairie grass. I figgered that the Colonel and Mr. Jebb thought they'd go back to Vicksburg to argue, this being the Fourth o' July, and they could take a day off from Hereafter.

# 14

## The Villain's Confession

---

**A**FTER THAT mystery of Johnny Reb's cap I didn't swear much for almost two months. A man's got to think after he runs into a thing like that. Ellis and I hunted all around again in the Waller, in the summer grass, and never found the cap nor any coyote tracks, so we agreed not to tell anybody and sound foolish. It didn't seem to me I was asleep when Ellis had chunked the firecrackers down on my ear.

July heat came on and big rains with it. Thunderstorms made the cattle stray; and one day we had to report that Effie's favorite old milker, Susie, didn't turn up. We rode all around a few miles and asked at Gebauer's and Webel's over south. Gebauer was away, but we explained to Miss Frawleen and understood her pretty well by now after she'd been more than a year out of the Old Country. Effie told me to thank her again for pulling me out of the snow last winter, but when I did she just broke into smiles and rattled on in German, and we were pretty good friends.

Earl Staley came back from Custer County and said he had a roof on and a well dug but no first-breakin' land for a crop. The mustangs he had wouldn't have pulled a plow even if he'd had one. I don't know what the feller was

214

thinking about, even to try getting married, except that
Effie was working on his mind.

Marion Marlow hadn't gone back to Texas, and I didn't
know what was on his mind either. Except one day he
asked me, "Looky, Chick, am I in the way around here,
comin' to yore place to see Earl?"

"Welcome as flowers in May, as Effie says. But stay
away from Gebauer's. Don't monkey around Miss Frawleen."

"Oh, I ain't in the way if that's what Effie's worryin'
about. Just devilin' around like I do with women. And
they get me in trouble. That's why I——" Then he broke
off, wouldn't say another word. He was young and brown
and thin now, as if he'd worried over something. He
stared at me so long that I stuttered and talked of something else.

"Seen that ol' roan milker of Effie's over round south?"
I asked.

"Yeh. She was in a little bunch of animals over toward
Plum Crick. Thought mebbe you folks'd sold her."

"Effie wouldn't sell Susie no time. Next time you ridin'
this way bring her home. Much obliged."

"If I do come this way. I rode over to tell Earl mebbe
I better pull freight fer Texas so's to save trouble."

"You're no trouble. Effie used to hope you an' Earl'd
git in a fight over that girl, like in her book, but she's give
it up."

Marion picked up his reins. "No durn woman's ever
goin' to git me an' Earl in any rookus. He taught me about
all I know in cattle business." He touched his animal and
started. "Tell Earl I got to see him afore I pull out. If he

got married, damn if I know when I'd see him ag'in."

"Well, he ain't married yet. Ain't even worryin' about it, I guess—if Effie'd let him alone. An' Miss Frawleen, Earl ain't even asked her, I bet. Scared to. You got a lot of gall, why don't you ask her fer him? You know how to talk to women."

"An' git myself in a mess? If Miss Frawleen don't know yet she's goin' to git married, plans laid an' all fer a weddin', why don't you go ask her fer Earl?"

"Me? An' git *myself* in a mess! I don't fool with women!"

Marion just rode on, laughing, some of his Mexican buttons kind of loose and jingling. It made me mad when I felt so grown-up now and able to cuss again, except I wouldn't cuss at the Buffalo Waller where Mr. Jebb and the Colonel had scolded me even if they were just another Mystery. But the older I got, the more I got tangled up with Mysteries. So I said, To heck with 'em! I don't want to learn anything more.

I tried to keep the dictionary book out of the leaks in our dugout and scraped mud off it, but that was far as I'd go to please Effie, who wanted me to learn the whole thing.

When I got home and told her that Marion Marlow had seen her little roan cow off south with Mr. Gebauer's bunch, right away she said for me to hunt up Earl and get the critter back. Ol' Tops was on his feet again after his colic, so I rode south, and it was a fine morning after big rains. The prairie sloughs were full and the red-winged blackbirds happy again. I found some cattle away off toward Plum Creek, a dozen milk muleys and two range steers, but no Susie-cow with them. Then I saw a lone rider and rode over to ask him, and there was Earl Staley himself, mooning around as if he didn't want to talk to anybody. That man had begun to act queer like a loco cow himself. He just said hello, and I said hello. Then for once I didn't know what to say. Bad as talking to ghosts.

He hadn't seen Effie's milk cow, but when I told him that Marion had down near Plum Crick we started that way.

"That feller says he's goin' away soon an' wants to see you first," I said.

"Goin' away? An' never told me?" Earl looked worried again. "That boy'll git in more trouble if he goes to Texas."

"What kind o' trouble has he been in?"

"Never mind," said Earl. "I got to find him today."

"It's on account o' you an' Miss Frawleen gittin' married he's goin' away."

"Who said that? I ain't doin' any such thing!"

"Then you better light out fer Texas with Marion. Effie's goin' to git you married afore Christmas."

"Like hell," said Earl, and he looked pretty dismal.

Well, we rode on, crossed some little draws that were half full of water dancing along, and I felt happy with the sun and grass and birds, and gophers coming out to play. Here this cowhand just rode along slow to keep with Tops and was gloomy all the time. Finally we saw the line of trees that marked the river Ellis and I had discovered, and there were a few more farm cattle near the trees. We rounded them up, and no Susie-cow. We rode along the creek, and it was a sight for me. Full of brown roaring water under the trees, and the little flat where Ellis and I had bedded down in the plum thickets from the prairie fire was covered deep with water and brush and floating trees.

Earl wasn't excited. He'd seen floods before, but I hadn't. When we rounded a point I yelled at him, "There's ol' Susie, an' tied up to some bushes!"

"Now, who done that? She's wet like she's been half drowned."

"Yeh, somebody roped an' snaked her outa the crick."

Earl got off his pony and slid down the mudbank. "Somebody who did it was Marion. This is his rope on her. Then where's he at?"

Earl floundered on along a caving bank. Big fast water on one side and the half-drowned plum trees on the other. Earl went around them and then called me, very quiet. "Come here, Chick. I don't aim to like this. I don't see his horse anywhere, an' that cowhand wouldn't leave his critter in a spot like this."

"He roped Effie's cow an' dragged her out."

"Yeh, but where's he? That boy can't swim any more 'n you can. Come on, Chick. The bank's caved along here."

We went on foot around a bend, and it had caved, all yellow clay under the top sod. Then I saw Marion's hat— the big Mexican hat with the fancy bangles on it—and it was floating slowly in a bend. Earl just stared and went on. Around the bend he pointed. There was Marion's pinto pony, shining-wet, saddled and reins dropped. The little horse looked at us sorry-like. Marion's raincoat and his Winchester were there with his little pack, and maybe he had started for Texas and wound up getting drowned trying to save Effie's cow.

Earl said, "You go back, Chick. I'm goin' to find my friend along this bottom if I hunt day an' night."

"Me too, Earl. Takes men to handle job like this."

"Go on down the creek an' look."

Well, I did. If this feller Marion was drowned, then maybe we'd have a funeral, and I'd never seen one or a weddin' either. I was clear out of sight of Earl when I heard somebody shout. Weak and far off, it seemed.

I waded around some plum trees flat over in the water, and out in the flood was an old snag floating along. And hanging to it was Marion Marlow. I might not have seen him except that some of the cowboy buttons on the line of his pants shone in the sun. He turned his face, all streaked with mud and scratches. "Hey, Chick! I can't git to shore. Where's my horse?"

"All right. You hang on." I ran back and yelled.

Earl came loping around the bushes. He stopped and stared.

"He can't swim. I can't swim. Nobody can swim."

Marion was floating, but the old snag held him under water most of the time. Then it struck something and turned over. I didn't see Marion now. Earl yelled and dashed down the bank. I went with him and grabbed a branch of a tree and waded to my waist. Marion's leg with the shiny buttons came up, and I just touched him with the pole. Then Earl grabbed me and shoved me out, hanging to my arm. Then I could drag the branch over Marion's head, and he grabbed it.

Earl yelled, "Hang on, everybody! Slew him to the bank, boy!"

That's what I did. Got him closer, and Earl grabbed him. Then we were all sprawled out in the mud under the bank, trying to get our breath. Mud kept caving on us. So Earl got to the top and dragged the whole outfit up onto the grass.

Marion could hardly talk, but he said, "My critter all right?"

"Yeh. An' Effie's cow," said Earl.

"Dang the cow!" I said. "Marion roped her an' got dragged off the bank when it caved. That's what."

"That's it." Marion spit out a lot of mud and water and sat up.

"That's bad water in the bend below here," said Earl. "You drifted in there, we couldn'ta got you. Chick saved you, feller. He heard you yelp an' got the pole."

"But if Earl hadn't grabbed me, I'd been dragged in too."

"Hell of a mess fer three cowhands to git into," Marion sputtered. "This outfit ought to learn to swim."

Then he got on his feet and weaved on, anxious about his pony. Susie the cow was beyond, eating grass, not caring what this outfit did. Marion went to his horse first and talked low to it. Earl got his animal. But Ol' Tops stood away off, looking at the flood. He wasn't going to save anybody. Then I thought about the dog in the Second Reader that jumps in and saves the boy. Two of our dogs, Tige and Bluch, had followed us, and there they sat, not interested a bit. Just scratched fleas. Goes to show you can't believe what's in the Readers.

Earl said, "Well, let's slope out fer home."

Marion sat down again, kind of weak. "No, I ain't goin' near Effie ag'in. It's home fer you an' Chick, but not me. I'm goin' back where I belong—in jail!"

"Shut up!" Earl yelled, mad as could be.

"No, I won't. It's due Chick to know, him savin' my hide. I'm a feller under false pretenses, an' I'm sick of it."

"You close yore trap!" Earl roared. "Wanta make plumb fools outa me an' everybody?"

"You ain't no fool. Yore the best pal a pore cowhand ever had. I'm tellin' Chick, an' you can't stop it."

Earl looked pretty grim at me. "Look here, Chick, if this dang fool can't be stopped, I want you to stop. Don't tell Effie or—well, Miss Frawleen—what he's gabbin' about, jail an' all."

"I won't ever tell anybody. It's just between us men."

Nobody batted an eye when I said "us men," and I didn't weigh a hundred pounds, I guess. Marion borrowed a chew from Earl's wet plug and grinned at me. "Chick, I'm just a triflin' fool."

"Yore one o' the best hands I ever rode with," said Earl.

"I got all I know from you. Now look, Chick, I give you the whole spread an' you do as you please. Last summer everybody admired fer to see my fancy clothes. Well, I wasn't in Mexico ever. I sent to Chicago fer that cheap measly outfit which I had to wear in the Kickapoo Medicine Show with a bunch o' Indians an' all, all painted up with feathers. The whole outfit, you can state, no good. We'd go into a town an' peddle medicine, dollar a throw, and then I'd do some ropin', an' them warriors would dance an' pound drums. But I made good money—an' spent it all. Came out here busted the last time, an' Earl he staked me with all he had. That's why the pore feller dassent git married."

"Who's talkin' about me git married?" said Earl.

"Chick an' me are. We're goin' to fix it. An' don't squawk. I'm tellin' you to shut up now."

"This is the dangest game I ever got into," Earl said.

"Well, I play it out an' hightail fer Texas. No more show business even if it was good money."

"Medicine show?" I said. "That's what Effie smelled on you. Camphor?"

"Not the last time, it wasn't. I takes a drink an' gits in a fight with the manager over a chippie. So I gits in jailhouse. Sheriff was a pretty good feller, an' he stowed my fancy clothes in camphor while I did three months. That's when I come up here an' Effie smelled camphor. But the second time I smelled funny, hell, no! It was jail smell, that's what. No sooner I got out fer that fight, dang near killin' the show manager, than I met the sheriff an' shoved him through a winda. Don't ever shove sheriffs around. It makes 'em mad. So this sheriff he shoves me in jail ag'in, an' I was wearin' my Mexican show outfit an' it got that jail smell, stuff they put on the bunks fer bugs. I smelled like hell when I started up here, that's a fact. But it fooled Effie, she never bein' in jail. That's one time we fooled her. Chick, someday you tell her what a triflin' fool I was."

"No, he don't," said Earl. "Nobody does that."

"Not me," I said. "But, long as everybody's confessin', I will too. I dang near got in jail on account of a sheriff came down here lookin' fer yore bones."

"My bones? What fer anybody want my bones?"

"Well, it was me makin' excitement fer Effie. I said

you an' Earl had a fight over that long-legged German girl an' Earl shot you. I saw buzzards an' saw something like a bone. Well, just goes to show how a well-meanin' man can make mistakes."

"Yeh," said Marion. "Like Earl here, busted on account o' bail bonds an' lawyers, tryin' to keep me out o' jail."

Earl said, "Oh, hell! Shut up—both o' you!"

Marion said, "Oh, it's all right. I like excitement too." He twisted another button off his buckaroo pants. "Chick, you take this home fer Effie to remember me by. Ain't it hell now?" He went to pat his little wet horse. "Now I squared myself confessin', I'm high-tailin' fer Texas. No more medicine-show pants fer me."

He borrowed a chew off Earl's plug and put a leg over his pony. "Now remember, boys, an' Chick's a witness: every cent I make I'm sendin' back here to Earl, pay up so he can git married." He rode off, wavin' his hat.

Earl looked dang solemn. He said, "That feller's got to come visit me when I git . . . when I . . . but hell, no, I ain't! Hear me, Chick?"

I had to ride home straddling behind Earl, and his cow horse didn't much like it. My critter, Ol' Tops, was a mile off north, heading home. The two dogs were trotting along at Tops's heels. Too much excitement for them, I reckon. They didn't care what happened to our outfit. The Susie-cow was ahead of them. Topping a little draw in the prairie, Earl looked back without a word. I did too, and I didn't say anything either.

We could just see Marion Marlow heading for Texas, smaller and smaller, but once, away off, fading out, I saw him wave his Mexican hat which had drifted ashore.

Earl said, "I bet the dang fool is singin' ag'in."

That's the last I ever saw of the cow feller who Effie once aimed to be the villain like in her book and get into a gunfight with Earl over Miss Frawleen Worsenever. That-there book like the rest of 'em didn't seem to work out just right.

I put my hand down in my wet pants pocket, and there was a big brass button I'd picked up when we fished Marion onto the bank. I'd forgotten all about how we nearly ripped his shirt off, getting him out. That button made me remember that out at the Buffalo Waller I had, cached in the bullet box, two dimes Earl had given me last year for sneaking him grub when he'd been drinking. Well, I'd get 'em for Earl to help get married on. Earl and I were pretty good friends after he and Frawleen pulled me out of the snow, half dead, and now we'd got this big secret to keep about Marion in jail for fighting a sheriff. I wouldn't tell anybody. Menfolks got to stick together. So I rode to the ranch feeling pretty important. Now I had two buttons for keepsakes of that dang fool cowhand who got into a medicine show, whatever that was. I'd take mine out to the Waller and tie it to the hanged man's rope, and I'd give the other to Effie as Marion said. But how tell about Marion without saying he'd been in jail twice and Earl was broke from having to get him out? I knew Earl would leave it to me, as Lige and Ellis did when they needed me to lie 'em out of some mess.

# 15

# Wedding Presents

W HEN EARL and I reached Lige's ranch we were pretty dried out and we'd scraped a good deal of mud off ourselves. The dogs, Ol' Tops and the Susie-cow got home ahead of us.

That old cow was pretty muddy, and this made a problem for Earl and me just what kind of lie to tell Effie, for we had agreed not to say anything about Marion lighting out suddenly for Texas, half drowned as he'd been, and telling that stuff about the medicine show, cowboy clothes and being in jail and all.

It was pretty hard to lie to Effie, she so sharp listening.

Earl said, "Oh, yore cow's all right. She fell in the crick flood. Chick, he waded in an' saved her life."

Effie said, "Funny, now—Chick ain't big enough to pull a bogged cow out the mud. Now tell truth!"

I said, "Oh, Earl, he helped. I was nigh drownded myself, an' Earl jumps in, grabs the cow with one hand an' me with the other, an . . . an' . . . "

Earl punched me in the ribs. "Better keep still. I ain't good lyin' as you are."

"Where's Marion today?" Effie said.

"Oh, we didn't see him. I guess he's down at Gebauer's or somewhere fer dinner."

"How come you got a button off his pants stickin' from yore pocket?"

"Oh, that." I pulled that big brass button clear out, not wanting to say that Marion gave it to me for keepsakes. "Oh, I just found it on the road. It's fer you, Effie. Them Mexicans ain't good sewin' like you are."

Earl went out, scared she'd ask him. I went out fast as I could. He grunted when we got back of the corral. "Chick, we got to keep still. I ain't goin' to have folks know Marion was in jail."

"Yeh, us menfolks got to stick together. I won't tell a soul. But if it was me been in jail I'd be braggin' all over 'em at school. I'd be big as Jesse James. I'd tell 'em——"

"Dry up," said Earl. "Here comes Lige an' Ellis."

"Yeh. But I help Marion an' you out a fix, so now you got to help me to keep Effie from naggin' me."

"I ain't much good lyin'."

"It ain't lyin'. It's about marryin' Miss Frawleen Worsenever. Effie sayin' I can help, fer now Miss Frawleen likes me an' can understand English. Effie says——"

"Now, wait," Earl muttered an' looked pretty pale. "This is goin' too far. I ain't made up my mind about nothin' yet."

"Don't need to. Effie's made it up fer you. Me too."

"Well, fer God's sake, Chick, dry up! Don't let Lige hear what yore tryin' to back me into. Just like gittin' a bad critter loaded into a railroad chute. Now, you wait——"

Well, Ellis and Lige came up and started to unhitch, and Earl and me had to quit talking. But I got near him and whispered, "Look here, if I get that long-legs woman to say yes, if she knows enough in English, will you say yes too?"

"Now, Chick, this ain't fair. You dang smarty can't run me thisaway. I ain't got a work horse, I ain't got a plow ner wagon. I ain't got nothin' but two little cayuses an' a rifle an' saddle an' rope an' six-gun."

"No, on account o' standin' by yore friend Marion, gettin' him outa jail twice. An' Effie wonderin' how come you busted this summer, not a dime fer plug cut hardly— not, mebbe, a nickel——"

Earl he sidles over near Lige, pretty miserable.

Lige knew something was up, the cow all mud, and Earl and me all mud, and Earl looking like he didn't have a friend in the world. Ellis got near me and whispered, "Say, did Earl ask Miss Frawleen to git married an' she turned him down?"

"No, we ain't got that far yet. She ain't got enough sense in English to understand anyhow. Let me figger what to do."

Effie called that dinner was ready, and we all went in, but there wasn't much talk. Earl didn't dare open his mouth, for he wasn't good at lying like I was. But I wasn't good as a man ought to be. Effie watched me so sharp that it gave me creeps. I slid from the table and went out to the corral, whistling, and got Ol' Tops. Effie saw me and came to the door. "You didn't eat yore piece o' pie. Where you goin'?"

"Just moseyin' around to git dried off."

Then I saw Earl come boiling out past Effie, and he yelled at me, "Come back here, you dang fool!"

But I was heading south fast as Ol' Tops could leg it.

Everybody at Lige's was getting so down in the mouth and upset that somebody had to settle this. I aimed to get hold of Mr. Gebauer, who spoke pretty good English, and if I could get it through his Dutch head that now Miss Frawleen was going to get married, maybe he'd help me out. I'd have to make them all understand that Earl was suffering and everybody had to help him out. But I didn't have anybody to help me out. I'd perused around about four or five places in that dang dictionary, trying to find if it said anything about love, but hadn't located it.

But when I reached Gebauer's he'd gone to town. And Miss Frawleen Worsenever was out in the garden, picking tomater bugs off the tomaters. I rode up and yelled, "Hey!"

Right behind her was Gebauer's big flower garden, and she looked pretty nice, like she did at school first day when I put a frog on her neck. But she wasn't sore at me any more or me sore at her, I guess. Earl might have told her I wasn't such a mean one after all. She stood there, smiling, looking all pink with blue eyes, and she kept on smiling. Then she said, " 'Ello, Chick!"

"How you these days?"

"Fine!"

"You know enough now so yore fitten to talk English?"

"Oh, *yah*—yes. Sure I know. Lots."

"Then, look here. How about gittin' married?"

She stopped with a tomater bug in her hands. "Now, what you talk?"

"Git married, that's what."

"You crazy little boy!"

"Oh, hell, it ain't me! I wouldn't do it anyhow. Not

ever. It's you I'm after. Effie's done a lot of plannin'. I went up an' saw them Rooshin folks that got the fiddle. An' they got a little priest, an' Effie could go dig her Bible outa her trunk, an' Lige could git some whisky at Jake's place. It's all figgered out."

"Never did I hear such thing! Who I marry?"

"You ought to know. Earl Staley, that's who!"

"*Ach, du lieber!* Never I been asked. Earl never say to me a word!"

"Sure he won't. He's busted flatter 'n a pancake. Scared too."

"What he scared about? Me?"

"Yeh. All upset. Now what you say? I got to git home."

She looked at me a long time, then at her tomater bug, then at the ground. Then she began laughing. "You tell Earl come see me!"

That was enough for me. I turned Ol' Tops around, and he lit up the road fast as if he was young and headed for Californy again.

About half a mile from the ranch I saw Earl on his pinto, just riding around aimless, I guess, hoping to head me off before I could make him any more trouble. I went over near him and yelled, "Hey!"

He just looked at me and grumbled, "Where you been?"

"You know dang well where I been. Down to Gebauer's. There ain't anybody there except Miss Frawleen. So you light out down there an' see her. She's pickin' tomater bugs."

"The hell I will! What fer I do that?"

"She wants you to. Go see her an' git started to git married!"

"Now, look here, Chick, didn't I tell you many a time to keep out o' my business?"

"Well, it's all fixed now. I'm goin' home to tell Effie."

He headed Ol' Tops off so I couldn't ride. "You ain't tellin' nothin' till you tell me! Ought to cuff yore ears off! Ought to——" He stopped cussin' and began to mutter. "Well, I'm a son-av-a-gun! I'm a locoed son-av-a-gun! I'm——"

I pushed Tops around behind him. "You go ahead, git married!"

"Look here, you asked her that? What she say, now?"

"Told me to hustle up here an' start you down to see her."

"She wasn't sore or nothin'?"

"She laughed all over. You hustle down there. She's pickin' tomater bugs, an' she was all smiles at me. Go ahead."

I lit out for the house fast as Tops could leg it. Earl sat his pony awhile, thinking, and then he rode on south very slowly.

Effie came to the soddy door when I was near. "What's all the conniption about, you an' Earl out on the prairie yellin'?"

"It's big conniption! Goin' to have a weddin' sure. Like in yore dang book!"

Effie sat down in the shade and fanned herself. Then she began laughing. "Well, of all things! But I knew it!"

That wedding had me in up to my ears in no time. Earl didn't show up until breakfast the next day, and he wouldn't say much. But he grinned for the first time since

Marion left us so suddenly. He said to Effie, "Yeh, I guess it's all right. Looks like it."

Then he said to me when we were alone, "Chick, you got me hooked into this. But it's all right. In a way I been figurin' on sayin' something like that to that girl at Gebauer's, but I never knew how to start it. Now she's said she would, an' that's a fact."

"Effie says yore goin' to get the best dang cook in the county."

"Yeh, but nothin' to cook. Nothin' to cook it in if we had anythin' to cook. Sure, I got a soddy built over in Custer, an' door an' winda in it. But I ain't got a team fer first breakin' of my prairie, ner seed corn ner——"

"You wait. Effie says 'Love will find a way.'"

"Don't see how love goin' to get us a bed an' couple o' chairs. I got an old cookstove I found in town fer nothin'."

Well, it did look like a dang fix for a man. I told Effie what he was complaining about, and, sure enough, she said, "Love will find a way," and went to singing while she set bread. Effie was happy, but Lige seemed gloomy. "I hate to see that man go off permanent so far. It's near a hundred miles." He rubbed his ear. "Nobody fer seven-up snowed-in nights. I got to learn Ellis, that son o' mine, fer somethin' useful besides work."

Ellis also seemed to be cautious about getting Earl married. "I heard to git married you got to have a preacher. There ain't no preacher I ever heard of around here."

"Up at the Rooshins' they got kind of a preacher."

"Yeh, an' can't talk plain United States."

"Well, I guess he don't need to. Looky, Miss Frawleen can't either, but she's agreed to hook up. I'm hitchin' to

drive Effie up there, an' she can light into them Rooshins
an' explain what's wanted. An' see about gittin' the fiddle."

"Nobody here can play a fiddle."

"We'll bring the whole dang Rooshin outfit down to the
weddin'. Toby can understand some English an' he can
tell the priest feller. The priest can play the fiddle."

The people around there had little to do with the
Rooshin families. Didn't know much what to say. But
the Rooshins worked harder than anybody and were always cheerful to me. Lige was busy out in the fields and
Earl had gone off to town. I hitched Tops and Jewel, who
were sort of retired old horses now, to the wagon and drove
Effie up to Toby's. She went into the big whitewashed
house, but I went to their pasture, for they had the first
shorthorn bull I ever saw. Kind of a fat woolly animal with
hair over his horns and didn't look like he knew enough to
hook anybody like our old prairie stock did. Couple of the
little Rooshins came over and weren't so shy as the women,
who ran in the house when they saw me. Scared of strangers,
I guess.

Well, in no time I heard the dangest argument in the
house. Effie mostly, trying to talk, big Toby shouting
"Yah, yah" to her, and if he understood or not I didn't
know. But in about an hour Effie came out, and two
women with her in shawls over their heads, and they
smiled too. Effie had her arms full of some kind of jelly,
and she laughed when we drove away. "Why, they're
nice folks. We just didn't try to know 'em!"

"Yeh, but how about the fiddle?"

"They'll all come an' bring the fiddle. An' Toby said
a lot o' stuff to eat an' something to drink. Wanted me to

drink some Rooshin whisky, but I told him I didn't touch the vile stuff."

"You ought to brought it fer Lige. He's all upset about Earl gittin' married an' goin' away. When you have that weddin'?"

"Right soon. Git 'em started off to get settled on Earl's claim afore cold weather sets in."

"They ain't got a dang thing to housekeep on."

"Don't need much. Lige an' I didn't either when we broke down here on the way to Californy and took up this land. Now look, ain't we civilized? Took just eleven years!"

"Well, Earl says I ain't yet. But I was born in Missoury, wasn't I?"

"Sure, the Colonel fetched you to me afore you were two. Nobody can say you ain't civilized. Enough, anyhow."

Well, we got home, and Lige was in the dumps and Ellis predicting the whole thing would bust up if we had a preacher who didn't understand English—just a fiddle. This didn't bother Effie. Next day she made Lige quit work, and they went off south to see everybody, about five families we knew but never saw much of, everybody too busy to visit. Ellis and I were alone on the ranch when Earl rode in from town.

He seemed kind of cheered, like he'd had a drink, busted or not. When he said he was getting married the boys at Jake's set 'em up. But when we told him Effie was going to run this wedding off right next Saturday Earl got scared again. "Now, look here, that ain't treatin' a man right."

"Effie's gone off to invite everybody. The Webels, an'

if their boys come it's liable to be a fight like at school.
Then them Perkins folks 'way over on Plum Creek, an'
the Gebauers an' some folks I don't know. I bet we got
twenty folks here to see you git married."

Earl looked more scared than ever. "Chick, I ain't used
to it. Man ought to have time to consider. Besides, I ain't
got pot or pan to cook with, ner a milk cow, ner nothin'."

I said to him aside, "Marion's got a job by now, I bet.
First wages he'd send you, he said."

"Hush up, don't talk about Marion now. He's a wild
boy—mebbe in jail ag'in, an' I have to git him out somehow."

"No, he's goin' to be steady. Gittin' half drowned along
with Effie's cow straightened him up, I bet."

"Well, he'll try it anyhow. He can always git a job,
good hand like Marion, an' talk near as good as Effie when
he wants somethin'. Well, I got to shave an' go see Miss
Frawleen, I guess. Dunno what to say yet, me not havin'
a cookin' pot in my soddy. No milk cow—no nothin'."

After Earl had gone Ellis said, "Say, when folks git
married they got to have presents. What in hell we give
'em now?"

"Somethin'. Effie'll fix that. I'll give 'em that Stealer
dog who don't like me anyhow."

"I'll give 'em the busted Kentucky gun. Lige can give
'em a couple pigs, an' Effie some chickens. But they ain't
got a wagon or team, ner plow. Earl's goin' to be in a bad
fix, married."

"You wait. Effie'll fix it. She'll read that dang book
about love an' start this-yere weddin' off right. You just
trust Effie."

"We all got to do that anyhow, fer she'll run things the way she wants. Now about this weddin': she's plannin' to hitch the wagon an' go off invitin' people we never saw. She says folks that had babies an' all, 'way off south, an' Miss Frawleen went to help out in trouble."

"Dang babies! I hope they don't bring none to the weddin'."

Well, things got a little quieter that week. Effie off somewhere, driving the wagon. Lige working the North Eighty, plowing with his second team. Ellis and me puttering around the place. Earl didn't spend much time at the ranch now. Effie said he had to go off to the county seat to get a license, which was news to me. One day I was off south, hunting a stray cow again, when Tops and I went down a little gully into big grass. And there Miss Frawleen and Earl sat on the side, talking. All around them were little pink prairie roses and meadow larks singing. I stayed beyond the slough grass, hoping they'd kiss or something, but they just talked. So I rode back, and they never saw me. I didn't think any cowhand would ever walk so far to find wild roses with a girl, for they never seemed much account off a horse. Earl was certainly hooked now.

Effie found so many cleaning-up jobs to do at the house that Ellis and me lit out for the Waller right after breakfast and stayed till dinner and let her jaw. Some cow had walked over the dugout roof and broken through a lot of sod. We had to clean up and found the old dictionary pretty damp and moldy now. I prie'd the pages apart and dried it in the sun. Ellis said to get rid of the durn thing if I couldn't read it. But I figured it would do for a wedding present, Earl and Frawleen not knowing much as they ought to.

Ellis said, "It's too big to lug clear to Custer County. Anyhow, we got two books at home, all dusted off. Effie got her Bible out an' aired. She aims to have Earl an' Frawleen put their names in it. Fer keepsake. She got her storybook out too, an' her Californy dress which she never wore yet. I'm goin' to stay away from the house with all that excitement."

Minute we went there we had to work. Clean the yard, straighten up a couple of the windbreak trees and keep the dogs from barking at Effie's Californy dress airing on the line. They never saw anything pretty like that. But it still smelled of camphor, and that made me think of jail and Marion Marlow off riding for some outfit to get money to pay Earl and maybe not drinking any. A good thing that hellion wouldn't be at the wedding, for Toby said he was going to bring down a lot of Rooshin whisky and the fiddle.

Lige said, "Well, that saves me some money, the Mortgage comin' ag'in this fall an' the boys got to have boots, but mebbe Rooshin whisky'll knock everybody flat an' end the weddin'."

Effie said, "Don't bring no ol' whisky-heads from town an' there won't be trouble. Earl ain't a drinkin' man much, an' anyhow he's got to dance with Miss Frawleen."

I yelled, "You mean dance to git married? I never seen any dance, but where could folks dance?"

"Right out in front the soddy," said Effie. "There won't be room in the house, what with cookin' an' all."

She certainly cooked and all. Miss Frawleen came over

to help, and laughed and said, " 'Ello, Chick, you smarty—make me get married!"

"Don't go blamin' me fer it. It's on account of a book. Pink book, with yeller flowers on it."

Miss Worsenever looked puzzled, but she pitched in to help Effie. She made a lot of bread and meat stuck together which she called sandwiches, and I'd never heard of them before. But Effie was in the soddy baking, and everybody had to get out. When she baked anything there was always a big row. Her oven door was hung on with a piece of rusty bobbed wire and it wouldn't stay shut. So she had to prop the oven shut with her broom, the other end against the doorframe. So nobody could get in or out except dogs and cats who smelled cooking. The soddy door had a cloth screen against mosquitoes, and little cats had wormed a hole in it 'way last spring. Then bigger cats crawled in. The hole got bigger, and pretty soon in came pups. Then the big dogs, and they'd knock Effie's oven door open. You'd hear the dangest row ever when Effie cooked a big dinner.

Miss Frawleen stuck her head in, wanting to help. But Lige and Ellis and me went behind the corral and whittled sticks and listened, knowing better than get near the house. Miss Frawleen had her big pile of sandwiches on the wagon endgate, waiting for folks to come eat. But afterwhile she disappeared down to Gebauer's, driving his buggy, for now she'd got that much in her noodle even if she would never get on a horse again after I dumped her in the tank.

Well, the day before the weddin' Ellis said he smelled skunk out near the Waller. Effie gave me the worst look I ever saw. "Now, look here, Chick, yore the one who always gits the dogs and starts skunk-fightin'. Yore the only one in this family got a stomach to stand 'em. But if you git this weddin' to smell of skunk, I'll tie you up an' ship you Back East somewhere. Hear me?"

"Yeh," I said. "I promise."

But it was sure a big temptation. Only I didn't want to be shipped Back East, and this was one time when Effie looked pretty mad at me, and she'd do what she said.

# 16

# Moonlight, Roses—and Effie

---

**S**o the big day came. Effie said that when folks got married the woman had to have "something old and something new, something borrowed and something blue." She sang it like a little song, being so happy. Being busted, Earl couldn't get a wedding ring which was proper, but nobody cared. Effie got that little cracked vase out of her trunk which could be for old and blue. Earl would have a pair of store pants which were new. Mr. Gebauer would lend him a work team to start farming with, and that was borrowed.

So the whole thing was fixed proper. Effie disappeared down the road into Mr. Gebauer's flower garden, but she was back when folks began to arrive. Except for politics, I never saw so many people. Five wagons and about forty folks, and six or seven young riders who came whoopin' in from beyond Plum Creek. The Webels came, but we were all too polite to fight like at school. Some big girls came from somewhere, but Ellis and I stayed away from them, acting polite. Some women piled four baby-kids on a blanket in the soddy shade and let 'em yell. Ellis and I didn't go near 'em. Lige had to yank some boards off the corncrib to make the table long, and it was too long for the house, so Effie set it in the yard. With all the cooking there wasn't room for half the folks in the soddy anyhow. Menfolks sat along the corral fence, waiting to eat. Effie looked anxiously up North Road, for she'd had a time arguing with the Russian priest who said maybe it wasn't lawful for him to marry folks in this country. Effie told him nobody gave a dang, just bring his fiddle.

So down the Rooshins came, two wagons of them—four men and even three womenfolks who'd always been too shy to have anybody see them; and three boys who used to run into the house whenever they saw strangers. The Rooshin women all had black shawls over their heads, and they all stayed in a huddle, but they laughed when anybody spoke to them.

Effie made us all go and shake hands. "Now maybe they'll see we ain't hostile to 'em as they thought when they first came from the Old Country. Now we'll all git acquainted an' grow up with the country here."

Lige scratched his ear. Not for him. Someday he'd hitch and start for Californy again. But he wouldn't say so to anybody except Ellis and me.

Well, the sun got where it wasn't so hot, and menfolks wandered around from the corral over to Toby's wagon where the little pink-faced priest with his little black cap sat with his fiddle and laughed. Toby climbed up behind him, and he had a dipper and he began to dish out whisky to anybody who had a cup. Pretty soon there was a lot of talk. Women didn't drink in those days, so they stayed by the soddy where Effie had the table set, and she didn't have half enough plates for all of them.

Then the little priest in the wagon seat took his fiddle, and a couple of young fellers began to dance. One came and grabbed a girl and started to jig her around the yard, and everybody laughed again. It certainly was excitement, but Lige said, "Where's Earl? Did that dang-busted cow-hand scoot off an' leave us with no weddin'?"

Effie said, "You just wait. I fixed it."

Suddenly all the folks up by the soddy began to yell. The men around the wagon looked that way. Big Toby set his dipper down to see what was up. I was on the other side of the wagon, and I got hold of his dipper. That Rooshin whisky was certainly strong stuff. One swig made my hair crinkle, and my ears kind of popped. And for a minute I couldn't talk.

Then I came around the wagon and looked, and there was a sight I'd never expect to see all my born days. Lige was standing by me with a cup of whisky, but he set it down and said, "Well, sir, Chick, this is the first kick an' flicker o' civilization I ever see in these parts, dang if it ain't!"

Well, sir, it looked like that. Gebauer's buggy was just turning on from South Road, and in it sat Earl Staley and Miss Frawleen Worsenever, and they were all lathered up in flowers. Earl was shaved blue and had a new hat, and his hat was all flowers, and around his neck flowers, and Miss Frawleen had a white dress, but she was all covered in flowers. Some was little pink wild prairie roses, and the rest were every kind of flowers from the German's garden—and Gebauer raised a lot.

Even the spokes on the buggy was tied with little roses, and behind the buggy Mr. and Mrs. Gebauer rode in their wagon, and it was piled full of farm stuff. Gebauer stood up and shouted in German. Mrs. Gebauer couldn't speak a word of English, but she laughed and waved a parasol.

Everybody yelled. Earl Staley looked like he'd rather get run over by a stampede, but he certainly was hooked. Couldn't wiggle for flowers on him. And Frawleen laughing by his side.

Lige said, "Gimme a drink, Chick. Quick, gimme a drink!"

I said, "I bet Effie made 'em do that."

I grabbed the dipper and filled his cup. Then I licked off what was left. Big Toby was looking the other way and didn't see us. But he yelled in Rooshin to the little priest, and the fiddle began harder than ever. Everybody cheered and shouted. It was certainly bigger than politics for noise.

Pore old Earl climbed down and shook hands with all the women. He looked sort of crinkly in a brand-new blue suit, regular store clothes.

Lige took another drink and said, "Hey, Chick, mebbe you won't have to wear boots this winter, fer there goes some money I was savin' fer the Mortgage. Effie got holt of it an' says, 'Damn the Mortgage!' First time I ever heard Effie cuss. Come on, go shake with Earl."

Well, all the menfolks went next, and everybody shook hands. Miss Frawleen shook hands with the Rooshin women, and they laughed.

Somebody hauled the little priest out of the wagon and set him at a table, and he began to work his fiddle harder than ever. The young hands began to grab women again and dance and raised the yard full of dust. Miss Frawleen was grabbed, and they shook about every flower off her white dress. Earl he tried to dance once and quit. Just

sat down and grinned. Lige got him a cup of whisky, and
Earl wouldn't drink it. He said no, his weddin' night he
wouldn't take any drink.

Effie tried to talk, but nobody could hear what she said.
Then she ran into the soddy and out again with her Bible
with the paper off it, the first time I ever had a good look
at a Bible. But I didn't put any dirty paws on it.

Then Mr. Gebauer reached under the wagon seat and
pulled out a Bible. But it was Dutch, and nobody could
read it. Then Big Toby he lugged a Bible to the table.
But it was Rooshin, and nobody could read it either. Lige
piled 'em all up by the end of the table, and all the grown
folks got around to eat—chicken, ham, beefsteak, pie and
cake, salt-risin' bread and cookies. Wasn't enough chairs,
so some sat on the grass and others stood up. Ellis and I
knew we'd have to eat second table whenever company
came on account of our heathen manners, Effie always
said.

Well, this dinner started all right. Little priest laid his
fiddle alongside the stack of Bibles and pitched in to eat
with the rest, and they all laughed a lot. Earl and Frawleen sat at the other end the table. Earl looked pretty glum
till he shed most of the flowers off his neck, but Frawleen
kept laughing and jabbering Dutch, so excited that she
plumb forgot all the United States talk she knew. Everybody was around the table except them young riders from
over across Plum Creek whom I didn't know from Adam.
They still hung around that little whisky keg in the
Rooshins' wagon.

Everything was going fine, but nobody married yet far
as I knew, and that was the big thing I aimed to see. Then

Lige got up, weaving a little, and Effie watched him from down the table with Mrs. Gebauer and the Rooshin women. Ol' Lige waved his hand and began to roar, "Well, folks, as a gineral host yere I'm called on to make a few remarks——"

Effie shouted, "Nobody's called on you fer remarks!"

"That don't worry me any. As gineral host I can state I'm the oldest settler around yere. Started fer Californy from Wisconsin. Almost eleven years since my off horse died an' we squatted on this land. Effie an' me near froze the first winter camped in that ol' Californy wagon. Spring come an' Effie saw them little wild roses everywhere an' meadow larks singin'. So nothin' would do fer that woman but homestead right yere among 'em."

"Shut up," Effie said, but her little brown face wrinkled all up in smiles and she looked young like she did when she first saw prairie roses. "But it was pretty here."

Effie was holding two Rooshin babies so their mothers could eat, and now she hugged them tighter than ever. Lige weaved around some and waved a hand. "Well, folks, we're here assembled to pull off the first weddin' in this part o' the country. Chick an' Ellis never saw one yet, that's a fact. They said they thought a funeral would be more excitin', but——"

"Sit down!" Effie cried and almost shook a baby at him.

"Well, that's all, folks. Some you can't talk English, mebbe, an' come so far I hardly seen you afore, but you all know how to eat. Pitch in—welcome as flowers in May. An' we're goin' to have married yere Earl Staley— good cowhand as I ever saw but mebbe pretty dumb at farmin'—an' Miss Frawleen—well, dang, I fergot her real name, but the boys call her Miss Worsenever, an' it's good enough fer me.. Now, ol' Worsenever——"

"Sit down!" Effie shouted. "Somebody pull him down!"

"Welcome, Miss Worsenever! Welcome, Mr. Staley! Yore gittin' the only girl around here big enough to git married, an' damn good-lookin', kinda tall, havin' long legs——"

"Stop him!" Effie yelled, and now I thought she was going to throw a baby at him.

Lige just went on: "But Earl's long in the legs too. Long legs ain't no bar to matrimony around yere. Legs will run in that fambly. Whole lot o' babies'll come with long legs——"

I was standing by Effie, and she jerked me around. "Stop him, Chick! Crawl under the table an' grab him!"

So I ducked down among a lot of feet. It was always that way. When things got desperate folks always hollered for me.

Didn't faze ol' Lige. He licked his chops and started again. "An' if any party thinks it ain't lawful to git married in Rooshin, Earl an' Miss Frawleen can find a kind o' regular shoutin' Methody out in Custer County. Nobody cares a durn——"

I heard Effie shrieking for me to do something. I crawled around over women's feet, which was no way polite, and grabbed Lige's leg.

But he kept roaring on. "Folks around yere certainly startin' these young folks off right. Got a whole pile o' farmin' stuff, some of which ain't much good, but you give it. Earl an' Frawleen certainly go off fine. Why, when Effie an' me settled here on account o' roses we didn't have a pot to p—"

I heard Effie again. I got a tight hold on Lige's leg, and then he bucked his knee up and hit my nose. Knocked me dizzy. I crawled out to find a whiffletree to mash his head, I was that mad. But when I crawled up alongside Effie and she saw me she let go the babies and hustled me off around the soddy. "Chick, yore nose is bleedin', so you keep out o' sight. Worse luck ever fer a bride is to see blood on her weddin' day!"

"Aw, hell, it won't hurt nobody!"

No use arguing with that woman. I was all blood, and she headed me out across the prairie. I didn't know where to go out of sight except the old Buffalo Waller, which was almost like home. The sun was just about down, but I still heard them yelling at the wedding. I sat down by the dugout, and my nose stopped bleeding, but it was swollen big. I thought, Bad luck, hell! It's me had bad luck. Nothin' to eat yet an' won't see the weddin'. Wisht I had a swig of that Rooshin whisky.

Soon it got some dark with stars out. There wasn't so much racket at the ranch now, folks home in wagons. I could hear those young riders from Plum Creek kyoodlin' down South Road, whoopin' and shootin' in the air, so I knew the whisky was all gone. I wiped some blood off and just remembered Ellis and I had figured to give Earl weddin' presents. We didn't have much, but I'd intended to give him that Stealer dog who didn't like me on account of his tail. But we couldn't find a piece of rope at the ranch to tie him with for Custer County.

Then I saw that hanged man's noose hanging on the big steer's horns, and I lugged it back to the ranch.

Nearly everybody had gone home. I heard wagons rumble far off now. I saw lanterns near the soddy, so I sneaked around to the water tank and washed blood off pretty good so they wouldn't have bad luck. Then I tied the rope around Stealer's neck and dragged him along.

Effie and Lige and Gebauer were loading stuff in the old Californy wagon. Lige let another yip and heaved a rusty old rollin'-cutter plow to Earl. Then he saw me. "Hey, Chick! You an' Ellis got to sleep in the house now like civilized! Mr. Gebauer loaned Earl a work team to start first breakin' out on his claim, but he can't give a wagon. So Effie an' me give 'em the ol' covered wagon, an' here it starts west ag'in. What you givin' 'em? Weddin' presents?"

"Ol' Stealer dog an'—an' a rope to tie him." I went around to Earl in a hurry so Effie wouldn't notice it was the hanged man's rope. "Here y'are, Earl—weddin' present."

"Thanks, Chick. Ellis give us four cats. I'll sure need a rope out on the claim. Much obliged, boys."

"Yours truly," I said.

Effie smiled. "You boys can be real polite if you want."

Well, I wondered where Ellis and me would sleep hot nights. But we all pitched in to help load. They had the dangest lot of old stuff you ever could see. Chairs and table, and bedstead and boxes of home-canned tomaters, and I guess a ton of potaters and a side of beef, and two live shoats and a crate of chickens. It seems that everybody around there, folks we hardly knew, had pitched in, for

Miss Frawleen had gone around helping them with babies and all.

They were just about to start, Lige and Effie up by the team talking to Frawleen, and Earl at the endgate tying stuff on; Earl's two cow ponies tied behind the outfit.

He put his dog up on top the load, with the cats in a sack and the roosters squawking. He didn't know that rope had hanged a feller. Effie couldn't holler bad luck for brides maybe.

Well, we all yelled some more and shook hands again and Earl larruped his team. Off they started. The Californy wagon with old tattered canvas heading Out West again. Tops he put his head over the corral fence and nickered. The ol' critter seemed sad to see that outfit start west and he wasn't pulling it as he did when he was Californy-bound, big and stout, and all the world lay before his young hoofs. Effie went and put her hand on his neck and talked low, but they both looked west where the wagon was hard to see now in the moonlight.

Lige yelled, "You better stop somewhere's an' grease them axles. Creakin' powerful bad. I put grease on yer load."

Earl yelled back, and the wagon was creaking. That's the last I saw of them. Moonlight and roses. And chicken squawks.

Effie had her hand on Lige's arm as they started for the soddy. Looked like she was cryin', and I'd never seen anybody out in that country cry except baby-kids. Ol' Lige was talkin' low and kinda sweet like maybe when they were young. They went into the soddy, and after a while Effie put the lamp out.

Ellis and me wandered around back of the corral, hunting a place to sleep in the hay, nights getting cool. Then I just happened to remember something. "Look here, I never saw that weddin'! Helped fer weeks tryin' to git it fixed, an' now I never saw the durn thing!"

"Wasn't much. Earl an' Frawleen just stood up, an' the little priest jabbered in Rooshin. Then Effie made Earl an' Frawleen sign names in the back of her Bible, an' she packed it away ag'in in the Californy trunk so no one dirties it."

"Yeh, but didn't somebody get kissed or somethin'?"

"Naw. I guess Earl was too scared afore folks. An', say, the dangest thing! I saw his full name, an' it was Earl Cute Staley! Think o' that—Cute! He said it was on account his mother sayin' he was cute back in Arkansaw where he was born."

"That long-legged feller—cute! I bet Effie laughed."

"Yeh. So'd Frawleen. And I saw her real name—Westenhoffer. We been callin' her Miss Worsenever so long I'd fergot it. Anyhow, she always laughed about it. Say, Chick, yore nose is all swole!"

"Yeh. That's all I got out this weddin' an' never saw it. Let's go eat what's left on the table and crawl in the hay. An' we can smell whisky where the Rooshin wagon stood. I don't want no more weddin's even if I didn't see this one. Too much excitement."

We went to sleep in the moonlight. Afar I could still hear the wagon creak—headed west.

We helped clean up the place the next morning. Effie and Lige slept till nearly sunup. Everybody felt kind of solemn at breakfast as if the best friends we had had gone away. Lige said, "Aw, Effie, now, don't take on so. Hell, only about two days' travel to Custer County, an' they can come visit us. An' someday I'll have Gebauer come feed the stock, and we'll hitch an' go visit 'em a week. Mebbe then they'll have a whole mess o' babies."

"Yeh?" I said. "Well, if Ellis an' me can camp out in the wagon I can stand 'em. Frawleen babies might be different."

"Listen to Chick!" Effie smiled again. "Gittin' civilized!"

Ellis and me went off before noon to clean up the dugout in the old Buffalo Waller. And we certainly had a surprise! First we found where Earl'd had a wheel off, greasing the axle. Then we smelled coffee, and down in the Waller there'd been a grass fire. It was hardly cold yet.

Ellis yelled, "Now what in conniption? They camped here last night! Ain't been gone an hour!"

I was down in the dugout. "Just come in an' look here! They left a note wrote for Chick an' Ellis, it said. Looky, Earl wrote it on a piece o' pink paper Frawleen got fer a present."

Earl could write better than anybody around there, I guess. His big square letters stood out in lead pencil.

Hey, boys, got a hot axle here so we stopped for the night to grease up. Then the dugout looked so good inside, hay and all on the shelf for a bed, and Frawleen had my saddle for pillow. I used that big old book you had stored. Well, so long, boys. And, Chick, thank you for steering me into this wedding.

Yours truly,

Earl Staley

Below that Miss Frawleen had written:

"*Ich liebe dich*. Chick, I love you too."

FRIEDA WESTENHOFFER STALEY

It certainly made me stutter. I felt awful, her saying that. Nobody ever said they loved me. I grumbled to Ellis, "Don't you ever tell anybody an' git me into fights at school."

"Naw, but just think, a woman gittin' into the Waller, an' us hopin' nobody'd ever find it, out in the big grass."

We sat on the edge of the Waller and looked around. It was mighty peaceful, the sun high and meadow larks singing. Few little wild roses still growing in the dried mud at the lowest end where Old Longhorn had taken his last stand.

Ellis said, "Look, three years now since we first discovered it an' fixed it fer a secret fort. Lige had some big yarns about it fer us too. Pawnees an' Sioux fightin' fer it till the buffaloes was all gone."

"Lige could tell whoppers snowed-in days at the soddy. He figured we wanted Indians around, so he went to talkin' big about first settlers here."

He certainly had, forgetting that he himself was the first settler on this prairie. Him and Effie. Ellis and I walked home across the bright land. I looked back once into the Waller. The last longhorn's tips glistened where we'd shined them up. The busted Kentucky rifle was all polished, hanging by a piece of whang leather next the dugout door. Even that dried dead cow had got a hoof up again, and Ellis had polished it too. Frawleen had tidied up the hay bed and folded our old ragged blanket and cleaned the coffeepot. The Buffalo Waller had seen some sights, with Sioux and Pawnees fighting here, maybe a thousand years, and now a cowhand had slept in it with a girl from the Old Country and a dictionary.

Well, here Ellis and I stood again at our Center of America, only now it was hidden by asphalt instead of wild prairie grass. The Four Roads that led from the middle of America to Mystery were avenues each way through the mighty cornfields. When I saw a house it gleamed with paint.

I looked again to where the soddy must have stood. Nothing. Except food for a hungry world.

Ellis, sturdy, strong and eighty, said, "What do you remember most?"

"Lige shouting to some passing wagonman, 'Howdy, friend! Stop a piece with us an' eat!'"

"Yes, and Effie running from the soddy door, calling: 'Bring them young ones in outa that wind! Ellis, you run kill some roosters. Chick, you run git the buttermilk from the tank!'"

"Then, when the outfit pulled west again to find a homestead, hear Lige again: 'Shovel some wheat into this man's wagon, Ellis! Chick, you sack some pertaters an' turnips. Git a big punkin an' a sack o' beans! I'll unhook a side o' hog meat from the lean-to! . . . No, friend, you ain't payin' us.'"

I laughed. "And damn the Mortgage! Whatever happened to Earl and ol' Worsenever?"

"Growed up with the country! Earl did well, stock raising. Frawleen had four girls and three boys. She named the littlest one, kind of a runt and a squaller, after you, Chick."

"Earl and Frawleen got to be old folks too—but hard to believe. Like Lige and Effie . . ."

Ellis put in, "Effie! Say, I buried her in the Californy dress which she never wore once in forty years except at the Weddin'. At ninety-six she looked happy."

I said, "She always was."